Arbidol: an antiviral aga

Eve-Isabelle Pécheur
Stephen J. Polyak

Arbidol: an antiviral against globally prevalent viruses

A promising antiviral strategy

Éditions universitaires européennes

Imprint

Cover image: www.ingimage.com

Publisher:
Éditions universitaires européennes
is a trademark of
International Book Market Service Ltd., member of OmniScriptum Publishing Group
17 Meldrum Street, Beau Bassin 71504, Mauritius
Printed at: see last page
ISBN: 978-3-639-65346-5

TABLE OF CONTENTS

INTRODUCTION

Arbidol (ARB), a molecule synthesized in Russia in the early 70s, has been administered for decades in Russia and China against influenza, with no major adverse effects reported. Its vast potential as a broad-spectrum antiviral agent, defined through *in vitro* and *in vivo* studies, lends hope for its clinical use against various infectious diseases that are at present not therapeutically controlled.

We discovered that ARB had potent antiviral activity against the globally prevalent viruses of hepatitis C, hepatitis B and herpes-8, and against deadly pathogens such as the Ebola filovirus and the Tacaribe arenavirus, responsible for recent oubreaks of lethal hemorrhagic fever.

These data and the molecular mechanisms of the antiviral action of ARB will be exposed and discussed in this work.

Mechanism of Inhibition of Enveloped Virus Membrane Fusion by the Antiviral Drug Arbidol

Elodie Teissier[1], Giorgia Zandomeneghi[2], Antoine Loquet[1¤], Dimitri Lavillette[3,4,5], Jean-Pierre Lavergne[1], Roland Montserret[1], François-Loïc Cosset[3,4,5], Anja Böckmann[1], Beat H. Meier[2], François Penin[1]*, Eve-Isabelle Pécheur[1]*

1 Institut de Biologie et Chimie des Protéines, UMR 5086, CNRS, Université de Lyon, IFR128 BioSciences Gerland-Lyon Sud, Lyon, France, 2 Physical Chemistry, ETH-Zurich, Zurich, Switzerland, 3 Université de Lyon, UCB-Lyon1, IFR128, Lyon, France, 4 INSERM, U758, Lyon, France, 5 Ecole Normale Supérieure de Lyon, Lyon, France

Abstract

The broad-spectrum antiviral arbidol (Arb) inhibits cell entry of enveloped viruses by blocking viral fusion with host cell membrane. To better understand Arb mechanism of action, we investigated its interactions with phospholipids and membrane peptides. We demonstrate that Arb associates with phospholipids in the micromolar range. NMR reveals that Arb interacts with the polar head-group of phospholipid at the membrane interface. Fluorescence studies of interactions between Arb and either tryptophan derivatives or membrane peptides reconstituted into liposomes show that Arb interacts with tryptophan in the micromolar range. Interestingly, apparent binding affinities between lipids and tryptophan residues are comparable with those of Arb IC50 of the hepatitis C virus (HCV) membrane fusion. Since tryptophan residues of membrane proteins are known to bind preferentially at the membrane interface, these data suggest that Arb could increase the strength of virus glycoprotein's interactions with the membrane, due to a dual binding mode involving aromatic residues and phospholipids. The resulting complexation would inhibit the expected viral glycoprotein conformational changes required during the fusion process. Our findings pave the way towards the design of new drugs exhibiting Arb-like interfacial membrane binding properties to inhibit early steps of virus entry, i.e., attractive targets to combat viral infection.

Received September 2, 2010; Accepted November 28, 2010; Published January 25, 2011

Funding: Funding was provided by ANRS to E-IP and FP (www.anrs.fr) and European Research Council (ERC-2008-AdG-233130-HEPCENT) to F-LC. The funders had no role in study design, data collection and analysis, decision to publish, or preparation of the manuscript.

Competing Interests: The authors have declared that no competing interests exist.

- ¤ Current address: Department for NMR-Based Structural Biology, Max Planck Institute for Biophysical Chemistry, Göttingen, Germany

Introduction

Distinct from specific antiviral compounds that target key viral functions are a group of broad-spectrum medicinal drugs that were originally designed for other treatments [1–3] or targeted toward a number of viruses ([4]; reviewed in [5]). The advantage of this group of antivirals is that they have already met the pharmaco-logical criteria for medicinal drugs and are already approved for clinical use in some countries. Among these molecules, antiviral agents targeting viral entry of enveloped viruses are of major interest since they seize an early step in the viral life cycle, before damages have occurred to cells (recently reviewed in [6,7]), and since they can be incorporated into combinations of multiple drugs with different targets. One of these compounds, arbidol [Arb; 1H-indole-3-carboxylic acid, 6-bromo-4-[(dimethylamino)-methyl]-5-hydroxy-1-methyl-2-[(phenylthio)methyl]-, ethyl ester, monohy-drochloride; CAS Registry Number 131707-23-8 (Figure 1)], is already licensed in Russia and China, and is described as an anti-influenza drug with immunostimulant properties. Arb is in use for several years as prophylaxis and treatment for influenza A and B infections. It inhibits influenza virus-induced membrane fusion and may have the capacity to induce serum interferon [8]. Recent studies extended its inhibitory activity to other human viruses such as the respiratory syncytial virus, parainfluenza virus 3, rhinovirus 14, and hepatitis B virus (reviewed in [5,9]). We demonstrated that it also inhibits hepatitis C virus (HCV) infection in vitro, and HCV replication [10], HCV cell entry and membrane fusion using HCV pseudoparticles (HCVpp) and HCV grown in cell culture (HCVcc) [11,12]. Most recently, Ciliberto and coworkers demonstrated the efficacy of Arb derivatives at inhibiting HCV entry and replication into hepatoma cells in the low micromolar range [13]. HCV infection is a leading cause of liver diseases, including hepatocel-lular carcinoma, and therapeutic options are still limited (for recent reviews, see [14] and refs therein). There is thus an urgent need to develop efficient and well tolerated drugs to combat this virus.

Arb demonstrated a propensity to enter into hydrophobic interactions with membranes, and with membrane-like environ-ments such as detergent micelles [12]. Here we further characterize the mechanism of action of arbidol, and analyze at the molecular and atomic level the interactions of Arb with membranes, tryptophan-rich derivatives and peptides. We first examined how Arb inhibits HCV entry and membrane fusion using HCVpp of different genotypes, and found that Arb inhibition was genotype-independent. By combining surface plasmon resonance, fluorescence and NMR spectroscopy ap-proaches, we showed that Arb directly interacts with the phospholipid membrane interface, with an affinity in the micromolar range, comparable to the concentration inhibiting HCVpp membrane fusion by 50% (IC50). Arb also displayed micromolar affinity toward aromatic components of proteins such as tryptophan and derivatives, and toward peptides containing tryptophans and derived from HCV envelope glycoproteins. Altogether our results demonstrate that Arb interacts with the polar head of phospholipid membranes and protein motifs enriched in aromatic residues, suggesting that the inhibitory activity of Arb on HCV entry and fusion could involve both types of interactions.

Materials and Methods

Chemicals

Phosphatidylcholine from egg yolk (PC, 99% pure), dimyr-istoylphosphatidylcholine (DMPC, 99% pure), cholesterol (chol, 99% pure), lyso-phosphatidylcholine (lysoPC), dodecyl-phospho-choline (DPC), Triton X-100, tryptophan octyl ester hydrochlo-ride (TOE) and N-acetyl-L-tryptophanamide (NATA) were purchased from Sigma. Octadecyl rhodamine B chloride (R_{18}) was from Molecular Probes. The peptides used were part of the sequence of structural or non structural (NS) proteins of HCV and of the bovine viral diarrheal virus (BVDV). The amphiphilic helix of BVDV NS5A [15] and the transmembrane domain of HCV NS4A [16] were obtained as described previously. The peptides identified as important for HCV fusion [17] were purchased from Clonstar Biotech (90% purity) or Sigma Genosys (70% purity), respectively, and dissolved in DMSO before preparation of lipid:peptide mixtures. Arbidol [Arb, 1H-indole-3-carboxylic acid 6-bromo-4-[(dimethylamino)methyl]-5-hydroxy-1-methyl-2-[(phe-nylthio)methyl]-, ethyl ester, monohydrochloride (Figure 1)] was a kind gift from Stephen J. Polyak.

A

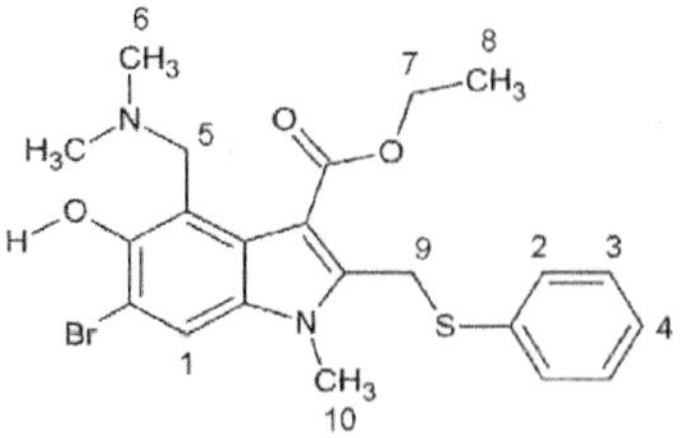

B

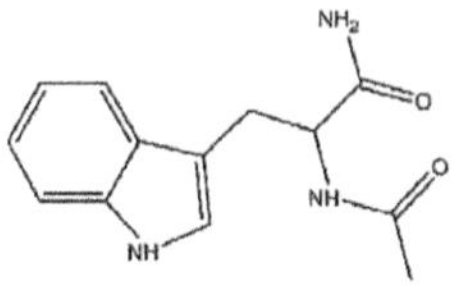

C

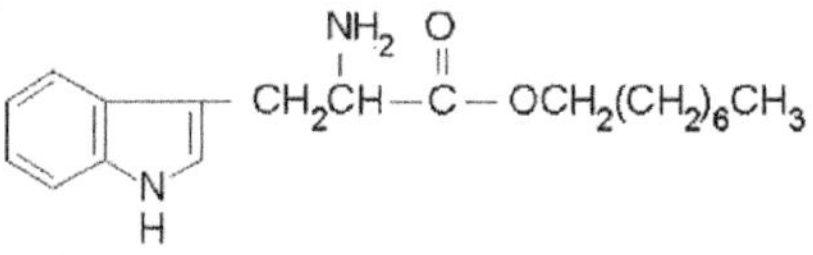

Figure 1. Chemical structures of arbidol (A), N-acetyl trypto-phanamide (NATA) (B), and tryptophan octyl ester (TOE) (C).

Note that numbering in panel A refers to proton numbers, as identified in NMR (cf Figure 5 and Table 1).

Arb preparation

Arb was readily soluble in ethanol, and soluble in the mM range in water. Ethanol stock solutions of Arb were diluted to a 1.88 mM final concentration in milliQ water (the final stock solution contained 10% ethanol). For SPR experiments, one mg of Arb was resuspended in water, followed by centrifugation (16,000xg, 15 min, 4°C). Arb concentration in solution was measured at 280 nm in the supernatant (Arb extinction coefficient = 9510 $M^{-1}.cm^{-1}$.

Liposomes and micelles preparation

Mixtures of lipids [DMPC; PC; PC:chol (70:30, M:M); PC:chol:R18 (65:30:5, molar)], of lipid:peptide (20:1, M:M), of lipid:TOE (20:1, M:M) or of detergent:TOE (800:1, M:M) were prepared in chloroform:methanol mixtures. After solvent evapo-ration, samples were resuspended in phosphate-buffered saline (PBS, pH 7.4) or water, and underwent 5 freeze/thaw cycles (liquid nitrogen and 37°C, respectively). Liposomes were prepared by extrusion over a stack of Avestin polycarbonate filters (100 nm), as described [18].

Cell infection assays

Huh-7 cells [19] were maintained in DMEM containing 4.5 g/ L d-glucose and 4 mM L-glutamine (Invitrogen, Cergy-Pontoise, France), supplemented with 100 U/ml penicillin, 100 µg/ml streptomycin and 10% FCS (Lonza). Productions of pseudotyped viruses were obtained by the transient transfection of 293T cells by the calcium-phosphate method. For the genotype study,

HCVpp of genotypes 1a (H77; AF011752), 1b (Con1; AJ238799), 2a (JFH1; AB047639), 2b (UKN2B 2.8, AY734983), 3a (UKN3A 1.28, AY734984), 4a (UKN4 21.16, AY734987), 5a (UKN5.14.4, AY785283) and 6a (UKN6.5.340, AY736194) were produced as described previously [20] from 293T cells co-transfected with a murine leukemia virus (MLV) Gag-Pol packaging construct, an MLV-based transfer vector encoding GFP as a marker protein, and the E1–E2 expression constructs.

Supernatants were collected 48h post-transfection and filtered on 0.45 μm. For genotypes 5a and 6a, pseudoparticles were concentrated 100-fold after ultracentrifugation through a 20% sucrose cushion at 75,000xg for 2h at 4°C. Pellets were resuspended in the regular medium of Huh-7 cells. For infection experiments, Huh-7 cells were seeded at 4000 cells/well in 96-well plates. The following day, cells were infected in the presence of increasing Arb concentrations for 6 h. Arbidol effect on viral infectivity was evaluated by assaying GFP activity 72 hours after infection using flow cytometry (FACScalibur). Pseudoparticles harbouring at their surface the influenza hemagglutinin (HApp) and the envelope glycoprotein of the RD114 feline oncovirus (Rd114pp) were prepared as described in [18] and [12], respectively.

Membrane fusion assays

Lipid mixing between pseudoparticles and PC:chol:R_{18} lipo-somes was monitored by fluorescent spectroscopy, as the dequenching of R_{18} [18]. In brief, R_{18}-labeled liposomes (1 μl, 12.5 μM final lipid concentration) were added to a 37°C-thermostated cuvette containing pseudoparticles in PBS pH 7.4 [viral titers: H77 (1a) $5.10e^5$; W529A-HC $10e^2$; Con1 (1b) $4.10e^4$; JFH1 (2a) $5.10e^4$; AY734983 (2b) $8.10e^4$; AY734984 (3a) $3.10e^4$; AY734987 (4a) $9.10e^4$; AY785283 (5a) $3.10e^4$; AY736194 (6a) $5.10e^3$; HA $8.10e^8$; Rd114 $2.10e^6$], and incubated 2 min. Fusion was initiated by acidification to pH 5 with HCl, and recorded on an SLM Aminco 8000 spectrofluorimeter over a 10-min time period, at excitation and emission wavelengths of 560 nm and 590 nm, respectively. Maximal R_{18} dequenching was measured after the addition of 0.1% Triton X-100 (final concentration) to the cuvette to lyse liposomes. The same procedure was used to follow pseudoparticle fusion in the presence of Arb; in this case, after a 1-min incubation of pseudoparticles with liposomes, Arb (11.3 μM final concentration) was added and incubated for 1 min, and fusion initiated by acidification.

Fluorescence assays

Indole emission fluorescence spectra of tryptophan derivatives were recorded at excitation wavelength of 286 nm (spectral zone of lowest absorption of Arb), under various conditions: NATA (5 μM final) in PBS at pH 7.4 or 5.0; TOE at 5 μM in lyso-PC micelles (TOE:lysoPC molar ratio 1:800), and in PC and PC:chol liposomes (TOE:lipid molar ratio 1:20); peptides at 5 μM in PC:chol liposomes (peptide:lipid molar ratio 1:20). Spectra were obtained in the absence or presence of increasing concentrations of Arb (0 to 100 μM). Samples were incubated 2 min at 37°C prior to recording. Emission spectra were collected in the 300–400 nm region (with 2 nm-increments), with blanks substracted, using a black flat-bottom, low-binding 96-well microplate (Greiner Bio-one). Measurements were recorded on a Tecan Infinite M1000 spectrofluorimeter. K_Dapp values were calculated from the difference between the areas under the spectra in the absence or presence of Arb

(ΔA), at various Arb concentrations, by nonlinear fitting using the equation $\Delta A = \Delta A_{max} C/(K_D+C)$. Fluorescence measurements were repeated three times to obtain averaged values of $K_D$app.

Preparation of giant unilamellar liposomes

GUVs were made by the electroformation method [21]. The flow chamber (Warner Instruments, Connecticut, USA) used for vesicle preparation was equipped with two glass coverslips, each coated with optically transparent and electrically conductive indium tin oxide (ITO) (Philips, Eindhoven, NL). Mixtures of lipids [PC:chol:R_{18} (65:30:5, molar ratio)] were prepared at 0.1 mM in chloroform. The lipid mixture (2 nmoles) was spread into a thin and uniform film on the conductive face of ITO-coated slide. After chloroform evaporation, the dried lipid film was hydrated by adding water into the chamber (ca 400 µl) and an alternative electrical field (10 Hz and 1.2V) was applied at room temperature for 3 hours. GUVs in the absence or presence of increasing amounts of Arb solubilized in water (0 to 40 nmoles), were observed by epifluorescence microscopy.

Surface plasmon resonance (SPR)

Interaction of Arb with DMPC layers was investigated with a BIAcore 3000 using a L1 sensor chip at 30°C. The sensor chip surface was washed with a mixture of 50 mM NaOH and isopropanol (6:4, v:v), at a flow rate of 20 µl/min for 1 min. The running buffer was milliQ water. The influence of liposome concentrations on the final SPR signal was tested; we assayed lipid concentrations from 0.5 to 5 mM and measured the resulting resonance units (RU). We obtained a well detectable, reproducible and stable signal from 2 mM, and further increasing this concentration did not improve the signal. We therefore chose the 2 mM concentration for our experiments. DMPC liposomes were resuspended in milliQ water and captured on sensor chip at 2 µl/min for 5 min. The flow rate was increased to 30 µl/min and the liposome surface was then washed with 10 mM NaOH for 1 min. Liposomes immobilized on the chip surface gave approx. a 5000 RU signal. To calculate Arb affinity for lipids, its association to and dissociation from DMPC layers were studied at different Arb concentrations in water, from 0.5 to 10 µM, at a flow rate of 20 µl/min. After each binding cycle, the sensor surface was regenerated to the original matrix by injecting 50 mM NaOH/ isopropanol (6:4, v:v). The sensor surface was then coated with a fresh liposome suspension for the next binding cycle. K_D values were calculated from the equilibrium resonance signal (R_{eq}) as a function of the analyte concentration. R_{eq} values were estimated by extrapolation to infinite time using plots of resonance signal as a function of the reciprocal of time. Apparent K_D were then calculated by nonlinear fitting to the expression $R_{eq} = R_{max}C/ (K_D+C)$, where R_{max} is the maximum binding capacity of the surface and C is the analyte concentration, using the SigmaPlot software.

NMR samples

For the NMR studies, the bicellar system was prepared by mixing 54 mg of 1,2-Dihexanoyl-sn-glycero-3-phosphocholine (DHPC) and 40 mg of DMPC with 400 µl of D_2O. The sample with a lipid molar ratio [DMPC]/[DHPC] = 0.49 was subjected to 3 cycles of vortexing (2 min), heating to 313 K (20 min), vortexing (2 min) and cooling to 273 K (20 min). The clear lipid solution was then added to 2 mg Arb in powder, and then subjected again to the procedure of vortexing, heating, vortexing and cooling. The final molar ratio [Arb]/([DMPC]+[DHPC]) was 1/48, with [Arb] = 9.4 mM. Another sample with similar lipid concentration and higher Arb content (molar ratio 1/15) was also prepared. The amount of free Arb in Arb:DMPC mixture was estimated after rapid separation of lipids on ultrafiltration membrane (cutoff 5000 Da) and measure of Arb concentration in the ultrafiltrate at 280 nm. For Arb:DMPC molar ratio of 1:4 at neutral pH, free Arb was found to be lower that 0.2%. We thus concluded that the amount of free Arb in NMR samples was negligible.

D_2O from Cambridge Isotopes Lab (Cambridge, MA), and Gd(DTPA-BMA) was a generous gift of Klaus Zangger. All experiments were performed with freshly prepared samples.

NMR spectroscopy

^1H NMR experiments were performed on a Bruker DMX 400 spectrometer operating at a proton frequency of 400 MHz. Spectra were recorded with a 5 mm Triple Resonance Inverse TXI probe equipped with z-gradient. The p/2 pulse was 10.3 ms, the recycle delay was 3 s and solvent suppression with presatu-ration was used. 1D ^1H spectra were measured acquiring 120 scans. These spectra were used for the assignment of the drug signals together with 2D NOESY and $^1H/^{13}C$ HSQC spectra (data not shown). The assignment of the lipid resonances was derived from the comparison with data in the literature [22]. To obtain Paramagnetic Relaxation Enhancements (PRE), a solution of Gd(DTPA-BMA) in D_2O (60 mM) was added to the Arb/ bicelle sample. Two sets of experiments were performed to measure the proton T1 relaxation times on the Arb/bicelle samples were performed. In the first one [Arb]/[Lipids] = 1/15, T = 305 K and [Gd(DTPA-BMA)] = 0, 2.0, 2.9, 4.6, 6.3, 7.9 and 9.7 mM. In the second one, [Arb]/[Lipids] = 1/48, T = 310 K and [Gd(DTPA-BMA)] = 0, 1, 2 mM. Proton T1 times were measured by using inversion recovery experiments with an inter-pulse delay ranging between 5 ms and 13 s. Each measurement was repeated 3 times, adding 240 scans with a delay time between scans of 15 s. All the spectra were processed using matNMR [23]. The ^1H frequency scale is given in terms of chemical shift relative to the acetone signal used as an external reference (2.218 ppm).

Results

Differential arbidol inhibition of cell entry and membrane fusion of various HCVpp genotypes

We have previously shown that Arb could inhibit cell entry and membrane fusion of HCVpp of genotypes 1a, 1b and 2a [10,12], and HCVcc of genotype 2a [11]. Here we sought to investigate the effect of Arb on other major HCVpp genotypes as well. HCVpp infectivity toward Huh-7 cells, objectifying HCVpp entry, was assayed by counting cells positive for GFP (as the marker protein), incubated with or without increasing Arb concentrations for 6h (see Materials and Methods). A representative data set is shown in Figure S1A, and inhibition obtained for the highest concentration of Arb (11.3 μM) is presented in Figure 2A. The inhibitory effect of Arb on HCVpp cell entry depends on HCVpp genotype. Indeed, within biological intrinsic variability of HCVpp prepara-tion and samples, three cases could be distinguished: entry of HCVpp of genotypes 2a and 3a was inhibited by ca. 60%, while 1a, 1b and 2b exhibited a 40%-inhibition, but entry of genotypes 5a and 6a was weakly affected by the presence of Arb (Fig. 2A). The influence of Arb on HCVpp-mediated lipid mixing was assayed by fluorescence spectroscopy using fluorescent liposomes, as previously described [18]. Lipid mixing between HCVpp and liposomes was only observed at low pH and optimal at pH 5.0 [18]. In the presence of increasing Arb concentrations, lipid mixing was inhibited in an Arb dose-dependent manner (Figure S1B for HCVpp genotype 4a). In contrast to what was observed for HCVpp infectivity, the effect of 11.3 μM Arb on HCVpp-mediated membrane fusion (Figure 2B) was similar for all tested genotypes, with about 50% inhibition of membrane fusion activity. This indicates that membrane fusion inhibition by Arb is not genotype-dependent.

These data suggest that the differential inhibitory effect of Arb on HCVpp infectivity of various genotypes is likely due to a genotype-dependent modulation of HCV glycoproteins interaction with the cellular proteins (e.g. HCV receptors) involved in HCV cell entry. Conversely, Arb inhibition of HCVpp membrane fusion, as assessed by a in vitro model system where the only proteins present are the viral glycoproteins, could merely reflect the interaction of Arb on lipids and/or on motifs present in HCV glycoproteins of any genotype. To test these hypotheses, we further investigated Arb interaction properties with lipids and protein fragments using the approaches described in the following.

Arbidol interactions with lipid membranes

We previously showed that Arb could interact with liposomes and membrane-like environments such as detergent micelles [12]. We further investigated this feature by studying the interactions of Arb with giant unilamellar liposomes (GUV) by optical micros-copy (Figure 3). GUV are pure lipid bilayers, intrinsically flexible and unstable due to their very large size (in the range of tens of mm) [24]. Increasing Arb concentrations were added to the chamber where GUV composed of PC:chol were electroformed (see Methods section), with Arb-to-lipid molar ratios of 1:40, 1:20, 1:10, 1:1, 10:1 and 20:1. The GUV bilayer was unaffected by the presence of Arb up to a 1:20 Arb-to-lipid ratio, with occasional membrane flickerings (Fig. 3C and asterisk in Fig. 3E). At higher ratios, membrane inhomogeneities and invaginations appeared (Fig. 3F, asterisks in Fig. 3D), and a major overall membrane reorganization was observed at a 20:1 Arb-to-lipid ratio (Fig. 3G). Note that no lysis or membrane dislocation of GUV was observed

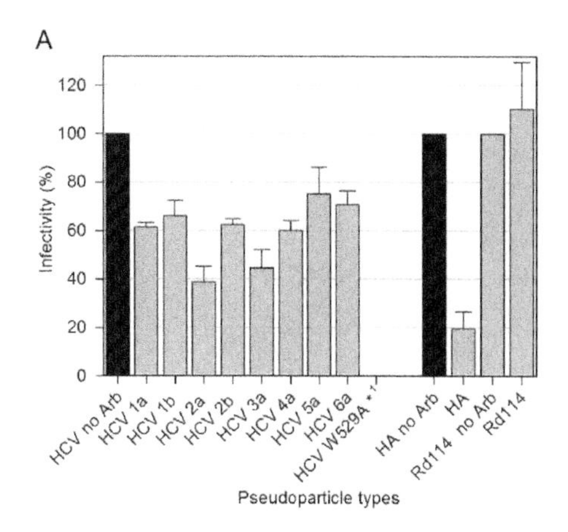

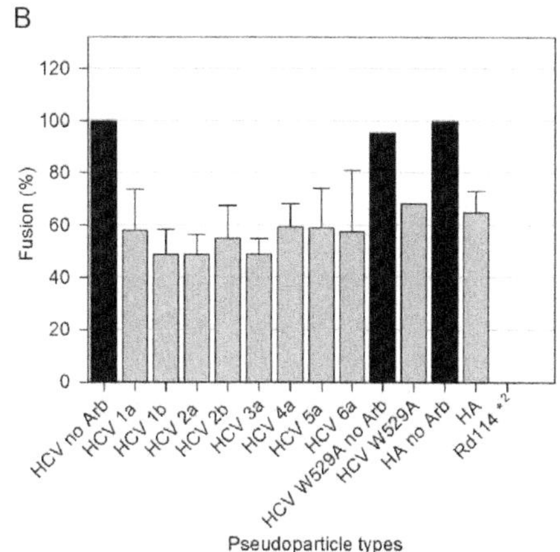

Figure 2. Arb inhibition of cell entry and membrane fusion of HCVpp of various genotypes.

A, HCV entry assays using HCVpp in the absence or presence of 11.3 μM arbidol. Huh-7 cells were infected by co-incubating HCVpp of indicated genotype with or without Arb for 6 h. Infectivity was evaluated after 72 h by counting the percentage of GFP-positive cells, using a high-throughput flow cytometer (FACScali-bur). The titer obtained in the absence of Arb was set to 100%, and the resulting percentages of infection in the presence of Arb were calculated. Results are the mean +/- SEM of 5 separate experiments. HApp are presented as control pseudoparticles sensitive to arbidol (cf also [10]), and Rd114pp insensitive to arbidol (cf also [12]). * [1], the mutant HCVpp W529A (cf [17]) are presented as a negative control of entry, displaying very low infectivity. B, Membrane fusion between HCVpp and R_{18}-labeled liposomes was measured by recording the kinetics of lipid mixing by fluorescence spectroscopy (excitation and emission wavelengths were 560 and 590 nm, respectively), as described in the Materials and Methods section. Values of the last 30 s of fusion kinetics (final extent of fusion) were used to calculate the percentage of fusion in the presence of Arb, relative to fusion kinetics without Arb (100%). Results are the mean +/- SEM of 4 separate experiments. HApp and mutant HCVpp W529A were taken as controls. * 2: no fusion was observed for Rd114pp.

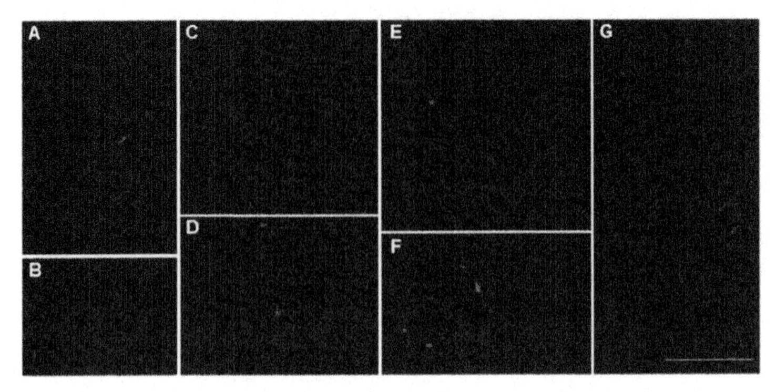

Figure 3. Arb interacts with lipid bilayers of giant unilamellar liposomes. GUV composed of PC:chol:R_{18} (2 nmol) were electroformed in water and observed by optical epi-fluorescence microscopy (A). Various concentrations of Arb in water were added to GUV, for final Arb-to-lipid molar ratios of: B, 1:40; C, 1:20; D, 1:10; E, 1:1; F, 10:1 and G. 20:1. Asterisks indicate small invaginations (panel D) or occasional GUV flickering (panel E). Bar, 25 μm.

for any condition, even at the highest ratio (data not shown). These results reveal that only very high concentrations of Arb with respect to lipids could significantly perturb the lipid organization of these bilayers. This also indicates that the direct interaction of Arb to lipid bilayers at the concentrations used to inhibit HCVpp infectivity and membrane fusion (panel E) do not perturb lipid organization.

In addition, HCVpp pre-incubated at neutral or acidic pH with Arb, even at very high concentrations (100 μM), displayed similar morphology (visualized by transmission electron microscopy) as those observed in the absence of the drug (data not shown). Indeed we counted over 160 HCVpp for each condition, and no difference in HCVpp morphology could be observed between the parameters assessed. This indicates that Arb inhibition of HCVpp fusion is not due to viral particle disruption/damage.

Surface plasmon resonance

To gain insight into the molecular details of the interaction of Arb with lipid membranes, we next investigated the lipid binding properties of Arb by using surface plasmon resonance (SPR, Biacore technology). We used a Biacore's L1 sensor chip to capture DMPC liposomes. This sensor chip displays lipophilic groups attached on the surface of a carboxymethylated dextran layer, and was shown to provide a quick and reproducible method for the preparation of bilayer-mimetic systems [25]. We first tested whether arbidol per se could bind or not to the chip. Arb at 11.3 μM (the highest concentration relevant in the biological context) was injected onto the chip devoid of liposomes. This led to approx. 60 resonance units (RU, see Methods section). DMPC liposomes (2 mM) captured onto the sensor chip reached about 5000 RU, and a further ca 600 RU was seen when Arb was pulsed onto the liposome-coated chip. The binding of arbidol alone on the L1 chip remains therefore negligible.

Measures of Arb/DMPC association and dissociation were performed with various Arb concentrations ranging from 0.5 to 11.3 μM. After passage over the surface of the sensor chip, Arb bound to immobilized DMPC in a concentration-dependent manner (Figure 4). Arb initial binding was fast, but then slowed down without reaching saturation equilibrium (from 0 to 240 s). After stopping the Arb flow onto the sensor chip (from 240 s), bound Arb was rapidly but incompletely dissociated from DMPC membranes. Indeed, for all Arb concentrations tested, about 50% of Arb remained bound to DMPC. This demonstrates that Arb is capable of interacting with lipid membranes, in a stable association between Arb and DMPC. However the behaviour of Arb binding to membranes rendered difficult the fitting of a kinetic model to the data, and hence the determination of reliable on- and off-rates. Indeed using global fitting, binding curves could not be fitted properly with the different models included in the BIAevalution 3.0 software (1:1 Langmuir binding, bivalent analyte, heterogeneous ligand, heterogeneous analyte, conformational change), with or without mass transport. Furthermore, because equilibrium was not reached during the association phase, the direct use of Scatchard analysis to calculate the apparent equilibrium dissociation constant was not allowed. Instead, the apparent equilibrium dissociation constant K_D was calculated from the equilibrium resonance signal (R_{eq}) as a function of analyte concentration, R_{eq} values being estimated by extrapolation to infinite time using plots of resonance signal as a function of the reciprocal of time [26,27]. Apparent K_D was then calculated by nonlinear fitting to the expression $R_{eq} = R_{max}C/(K_D+C)$, where R_{max} is the maximum binding capacity of the surface and C is the analyte concentration, using SigmaPlot software. This calculation, performed on 4 separate experiments, gave an apparent K_D of 6.8+/-0.4 μM (see inset to Figure 4 for a representative experiment). This dissociation constant is in the same order as the IC50 of HCVpp fusion (11.3 μM). This result indicates that the inhibitory effect of Arb on HCVpp membrane fusion is at least in part deriving from Arb association to lipid membranes.

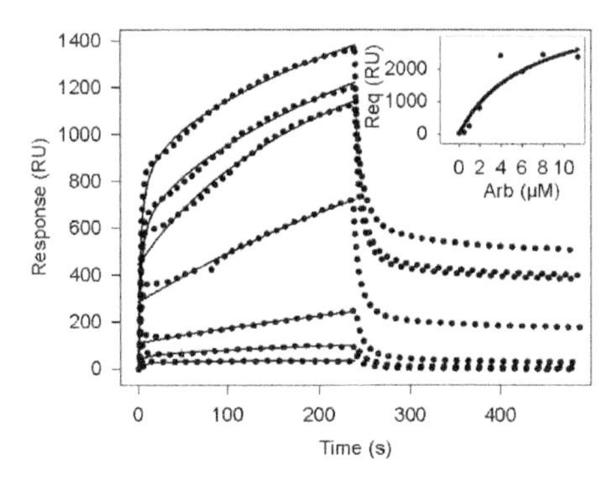

Figure 4. Binding of Arb to immobilized DMPC membranes. Arb in water at concentrations of 0.5, 1, 2, 4, 6, 8 and 11.3 μM was injected over immobilized DMPC membranes (ca. 5000 resonance units) for 4 min at a flow rate of 20 μl/min, followed by water. Blank curves without Arb were substracted from those obtained with Arb. Inset, representative set of data of non-linear regression fits to the equilibrium resonance signal (R_{eq}), obtained by extrapolation to infinite time (see Materials and Methods), vs Arb concentration, used to obtain apparent equilibrium dissociation constant (K_D) as well as the maximum binding capacities (R_{max}). Kinetics were reproduced 4 times. Dotted curves represent the sensorgram and solid curves the non-linear fit. RU, resonance units.

NMR experiments

NMR spectroscopy was used to characterize the Arb insertion in a model membrane system. The ^{1}H NMR spectrum of Arb recorded at 305 K in deuterated water is shown in Figure 5A (black spectrum), and the assignment of the proton signals deduced from 2D spectra analysis (data not shown) are reported in Table 1. In order to study Arb in a membrane-mimetic environment, we used isotropic phospholipid bicelles consisting of a mixture of DMPC/DHPC in water. Long-chain phospholipid molecules of DMPC self-assemble into planar bilayers, while the short-chain

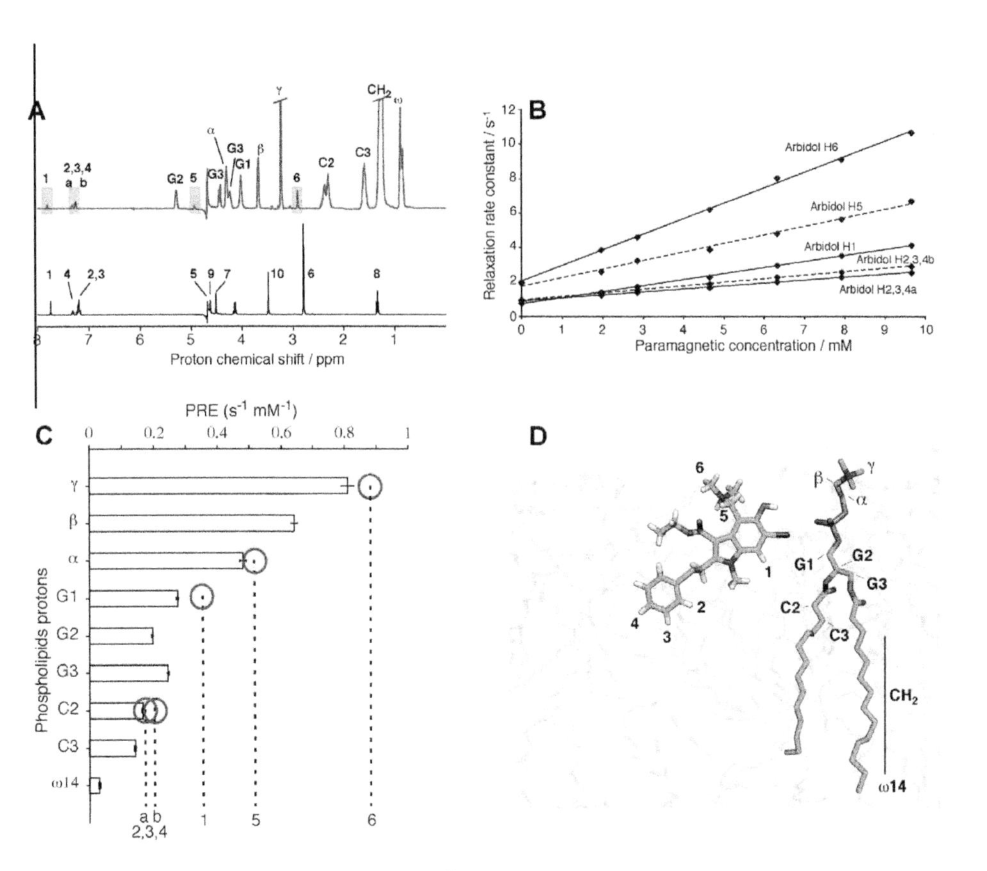

Figure 5. NMR of Arb into lipid bicelles. A, ^{1}H NMR spectrum of Arb in D_2O (in black) and in DMPC/DHPC bicelles (in red) with [Arb]/[lipids] = 1/15 and T = 305 K. B, influence of the concentration of the paramagnetic agent Gd(DTPA-BMA) on the proton relaxation times for Arb in the bicelle system. C, paramagnetic relaxation enhancements (PRE) measured on Arb (marked by dotted vertical lines) and on the phospholipid protons (marked by histogram bars). The phospholipid is used as a yardstick to roughly estimate the arbidol proton positions inside the membrane. Red circles indicate the yardstick marker closest to a given arbidol PRE value. Error bars indicate the standard deviation derived from the calculation of PRE. Error bars for Arbidol are comparable. D, sketch of the positioning of Arb in a DMPC membrane system. The Arb molecule was produced by generating an extended structure, and regularized by 1000 cycles of a Powell type minimization using XPLOR-NIH [69]. The positioning in the membrane system was done manually by taking into account the relative proton depth measured by the PRE (panel C).

Table 1. NMR assignment of ^{1}H chemical shift of Arb in water and in the presence of [DMPC]/[DHPC] bicelles at 305 K.

Arb protons	Arb in water (ppm)	Arb in bicelles (ppm)
1	7.75	7.81
02/04/10	7.18–7.34	7.25–7.33
5	4.63	4.93
6	2.8	2.92
7	4.15	nd
8	1.35	nd
9	4.52	4.68
10	3.5	3.67

nd, protons 7 and 8 could not be resolved from the lipid resonances (see Figure S2). Protons 9 and 10 can be resolved only in the $^{1}H/^{13}C$ HSQC spectrum.

molecules of DHPC segregate to edge regions of high curvature [28]. Bicelles with [DMPC]/[DHPC] molar ratio ,1 form fast and isotropically tumbling aggregates, amenable to solution NMR studies. Still, isotropic bicelle systems are used as a phospholipid bilayer mimetic, since DMPC has been shown to form a flat bilayered surface [29–31]. The ^{1}H NMR spectrum of Arb in this bicellar phase is shown in Figure 5A (red spectrum). In this system, the spectral crowding due to the presence of phospholipid resonances allowed only the observation of protons denoted 1, 2, 3, 4, 5 and 6 of the arbidol molecule (see Fig. 1A) where only 2 signals can be distinguished for the three protons 2, 3, 4. Additional ^{1}H resonances could be resolved from 2D ^{1}H NOESY spectra and $^{1}H/^{13}C$ HSQC spectra (Figure S2) and the corresponding chemical shifts are shown in Table 1 together with the assignment of the proton lines for Arb in water. Arbidol interaction with lipids induce chemical-shift changes in the Arb resonances when compared to that observed in water.

In order to investigate the immersion depth of Arb in the membrane, we monitored the proton longitudinal relaxation rate of Arb protons upon the addition of the soluble paramagnetic agent gadolinium-diethylenetriamine pentaacetic acid-bismethyla-mide Gd(DTPA-BMA) [32]. This paramagnetic contrast agent stays soluble in the water surrounding the membrane and induces a paramagnetic relaxation enhancement (PRE) on the spin of the atoms close to the surface of the membrane. Recently, PRE effects due to Gd(DTPA-BMA) were used to probe the immersion depth and orientation of an anti-microbial peptide [33,34]. Here we measured the proton T_1 relaxation times of both Arb and phospholipid protons to probe the immersion depth of Arb in the membrane, using the PRE values of the phospholipids as an approximated yardstick. A titration of Arb with Gd(DTPA-BMA) was performed at increasing concentrations of the paramagnetic agent, from 2.0 to 9.7 mM. At each step of the titration, the proton T1 relaxation times for the protons 1, 2, 3, 4, 5 and 6 of Arb, and for the protons alpha, beta, gamma, G1, G2, G3, C2, C3 and omega14 of the phospholipids, were measured. The plot in Figure 5B shows the relaxation times as a function of the Gd(DTPA-BMA) concentration. This titration leads to a curve for each proton whose slope corresponds to the PRE values. As shown in Fig. 5C, PRE measured on the Arb-bicelle system range from 0.90 sec^{-1} to 0.03 sec^{-1} for the phospholipid protons and from 0.90 sec^{-1} to 0.20 sec^{-1} for Arb protons. The PRE observed for each spin can be described as an overall relaxation enhancement [35], due to all the paramagnetic agents in solution. For a planar membrane surrounded by a buffer containing a non-interacting paramagnetic probe, the total PRE of a nucleus with immersion depth d is given by the equation [33,34]: $PRE = z/d^3$, where d is the immersion depth of a specific nucleus within the membrane plus the radius of the magnetic probe, and where the constant z is a combination of various parameters, among them a correlation time, itself a combination of the electron relaxation time, the lifetime of the intermolecular adduct bicelle-Gd(DTPA-BMA), and the rotational correlation time. In order to determine the immersion depth of Arb, instead of determining z, we used the phospholipids as a yardstick by comparing their PRE with the one of Arb.

The PREs of the resolved signals of Arb and phospholipids are reported and compared in Figure 5C. This procedure is based on two assumptions: (i) the amount of free Arb in solution in the presence of lipids is negligible (see NMR sample preparation in Experimental Procedure section), and it does therefore not affect significantly the PRE of Arb in the membrane ; ii) the constant z is the same for lipids and Arb.

Figure 5C shows that methyl protons 6 of Arb are at the lipid/ water interface as the gamma-proton of the hydrophilic head-group of the lipids. Protons 5 and 1 of Arb are at the level of respectively protons alpha and G1 of the phospholipids. The aromatic protons 2 and 3 are the most buried protons of Arb, close to the beginning of the hydrophobic chain (protons C2).

The validity of assumption (ii) is supported by the NOE cross-peaks detected between proton 1 of Arb and the glycerol moiety of phospholipids. In addition, the maximum PRE measured for Arb (protons 6) and phospholipids (c protons) are about the same, suggesting that the corresponding molecule regions are the most exposed to water. This estimation of the immersion depth of Arb protons relative to the phospholipids protons enables us to propose a model for the positioning of Arb in the membrane, shown in Figure 5D.

These NMR data clearly demonstrate that Arb interacts at the membrane interface, mainly at the level of phospholipid polar head. This result supports the assumption that the Arb inhibitory effect on HCVpp membrane fusion is dependent, at least in part, from this interaction.

Arbidol interaction with tryptophan derivatives and protein motifs

A second possibility regarding Arb activity is that Arb might interact with key motifs present in viral proteins, thereby impeding their structural reorganization at the onset of fusion and thus leading to fusion inhibition.

A first set of experiments was designed to investigate whether the order of addition of fusing partners would affect Arb-induced fusion inhibition. For this purpose, we measured fusion after pre-incubation of HCVpp or liposomes or both in the absence or presence of 11.3 μM Arb. As shown in Table 2, when Arb was pre-incubated with both partners before fusion was initiated by lowering the pH, fusion inhibition was ca. 50%. In contrast, only ca. 10% fusion inhibition was observed when Arb was pre-incubated with either HCVpp or liposomes. The greater inhibitory effect of Arb when it has simultaneously access to both viral and target membranes suggests that Arb could also act by interacting with selective residues of the HCV glycoprotein sequences.

This assumption was tested by studying the interaction behaviour of Arb with tryptophan (Trp) derivatives, as tryptophan is a constituent of proteins often found in regions located close to membrane interfaces, such as stem regions in several viral fusion proteins (e.g. HIV gp41 [36]). We also reasoned that Arb, being an indole derivative, might interact with tryptophan and tyrosine

Table 2. Influence of the order of addition of fusing partners on HCVpp 1a fusion inhibition by Arb.

Pre-incubation conditions				
Component	Time (min)	Component	Time (min)	Inhibition of fusion with Arb[a] (%)
HCVpp/liposomes	2	-	-	46+/-12
HCVpp	1	Liposomes	1	5+/-7
Liposomes	1	HCVpp	1	13+/-11

[a]Arb (11.3 μM) was pre-incubated sequentially with either HCVpp or R_{18}-labeled liposomes or both for the indicated times at 37°C before initiating lipid mixing by decreasing pH to 5.0 as described in the legend to Figure 2. The extent of inhibition of fusion by Arb was calculated relatively to the fusion observed in the absence of Arb and normalized to 100%. Results are the mean +/- SEM of 3 separate experiments.

residues through aromatic ring stacking. For this purpose, we tested the effect of increasing concentrations of Arb on the fluorescence of N-acetyl tryptophanamide (NATA) as a water-soluble Trp derivative, and tryptophan octyl-ester (TOE) as a membranotropic molecule (Figure 1B–C). The fluorescence of NATA and TOE was recorded between 300 and 400 nm, using an excitation wavelength of 286 nm, which corresponds to an absorption minimum of Arb [12]. Results are presented in Table 3 and Figure 6. The apparent affinity of Arb for indole of Trp derivatives was calculated as the difference (ΔA) between spectral areas (AUC) in the absence and presence of Arb (i.e. $\Delta A = AUC_{no\ Arb}–AUC_{Arb}$), for each Arb concentration at pH 7.4 or 5.0. Apparent K_D values were then calculated from the plots DA = f([Arb]), by non-linear fitting. Apparent K_D of Arb for NATA in solution was found in the range of ca. 60 μM at both pH (Table 3). Similarly, the K_D of Arb for TOE in lyso-PC micelles was in the 50 mM range at both pH. This indicates that Arb is able to interact with indole rings, but with a relatively low affinity. NMR analysis of Arb in dodecyl-phosphocho-line (DPC) micelles in the presence of TOE further confirmed this interaction (TOE/Arb/DPC molar ratios: 1:0.5:50; 1:1:50; 1:2:50 and 1:5:50). Indeed, chemical shift variations of aromatic protons from Arb and TOE were observed when comparing the NMR spectra of Arb/DPC, TOE/DPC, and Arb/TOE/DPC samples (data not shown).

In contrast, when Arb was added to TOE associated to liposomes (1:20, TOE/lipid molar ratio), a marked increase in affinity was observed (Table 3, compare TOE/micelles and TOE/ liposomes), reaching K_D values in the 10 μM range. Note that TOE fluorescence could not be measured in DPC micelles, due to a great intrinsic fluorescence of the DPC used for our experiments. Interestingly, these K_D values are comparable to Arb IC50 inhibition of HCVpp fusion (see above and Discussion section).. Indole fluorescence decreased when Arb concentration increased, with virtually no measurable fluorescence for 100 μM Arb (Figure 6). This further confirms that Arb interacts with indole rings, but with a higher affinity when indole is incorporated into lipid membranes. This affinity was higher for PC than for PC:chol liposomes (Table 3), and at neutral than at acidic pH (Table 3 and Figure 6). At acidic pH, Arb is most likely protonated in the lipid

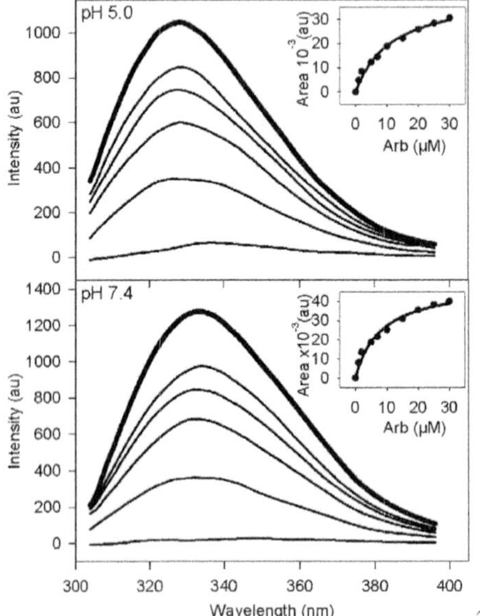

Figure 6. Indole emission fluorescence spectrum of TOE into PC:chol liposomes. PC:chol (70:30 molar ratio) liposomes containing TOE (5 μM final, lipid-to-TOE ratio 20:1) were equilibrated to 37°C in PBS at pH 7.4 or 5.0, in the absence (bold line) or presence (standard lines) of increasing concentrations of Arb (2, 5, 10, 25 and 100 μM). Indole fluorescence was measured between 300 and 400 nm, with excitation at 286 nm. The apparent affinity of Arb toward TOE was calculated from the plot of the difference DA between spectral areas (AUC) of TOE without or with Arb ($\Delta A = AUC_{no\ Arb}\text{-}AUC_{with\ Arb}$) as a function of Arb concentration (see inset for a range of Arb concentrations between 0 and 30 μM) (see K_D values reported in Table 3).

Table 3. Apparent dissociation constants between Arb and the indole ring of the tryptophan derivatives NATA and TOE.

Tryptophan derivatives and media	K_D (μM)[a]	
	pH 7.4	pH 5.0
NATA in solution	64+/-10	55+/-10
TOE in lyso-PC micelles[b]	58+/-9	48+/-4
TOE in PC liposomes[c]	6.0+/-0.5	9.2+/-0.2
TOE in PC:chol liposomes[c]	11.7+/-1.4	15.6+/-1.3

[a]For experimental details, see legend to Figure 6. [b]TOE-to lyso-PC molar ratio was 1:800. [c]TOE-to-lipid molar ratio was 1:20.

environment [12], as is probably TOE as well. Arb affinity for TOE under these conditions might then be lower than that of uncharged Arb at neutral pH, because of repulsive electrostatic interactions.

A third set of experiments was designed to assess the behaviour of Arb in the presence of aromatic residues into protein sequences, more specifically toward Trp present in peptides. For this purpose, we used synthetic membrane-binding peptides of known structure and containing only one tryptophan residue, expected to be localized at the membrane interface: the transmembrane helix of HCV NS4A protein [16] and the N-terminal amphipathic helix of BVDV NS5A protein interacting in-plane of the membrane interface [15]. Intrinsic tryptophan fluorescence of both peptides was monitored in the presence of increasing concentrations of Arb; this is illustrated in Figure 7 for HCV NS4A peptide inserted into PC:chol liposomes (and in Figure S3 for BVDV NS5A, 1:20 peptide-to-lipid molar ratio). The Arb dose-dependent quenching of tryptophan fluorescence at both neutral and acidic pH clearly indicates Arb interaction with both peptides (insets in Figure 7 and Fig. S3). For the NS4A peptide at both pH, a red shift of the spectral maximum, proportional to Arb concentration, accompanied the fluorescence quenching; this effect was more pronounced at acidic pH (6 nm at pH 7.4 for 5 μM Arb, and 12 nm at pH 5.0 for 100 μM Arb). This red shift suggests that Arb, when

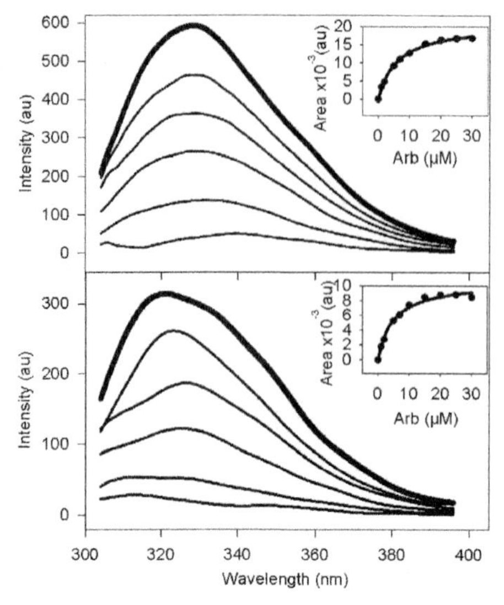

Figure 7. Trp emission fluorescence spectrum of an HCV model peptide into PC:chol liposomes. PC:chol (70:30 molar ratio) liposomes containing HCV NS4A peptide (KKGGSTWVLVGGVLAA-LAAYCLSTGSGGKK, 5 µM final, lipid-to-peptide ratio 20:1) were equili-brated to 37°C in PBS at pH 7.4 or 5.0, in the absence (bold line) or presence (standard lines) of increasing concentrations of Arb (2, 5, 10, 25 and 100 µM). Trp fluorescence was measured between 300 and 400 nm, with excitation at 286 nm. The apparent affinity of Arb toward Trp was calculated from the plot of the difference ΔA between areas under the curve (AUC) of peptide without or with Arb ($\Delta A = AUC_{no\ Arb} - AUC_{with\ Arb}$) as a function of Arb concentration (see inset for a range of Arb concentrations between 0 and 30 µM) (see K_D values reported in Table 4).

interacting with NS4A peptide, relocates its tryptophan residue to a more shallow zone of the membrane, where the Trp environment would be more hydrophilic. The measure of the apparent affinity of Arb for these peptides inserted into PC:chol liposomes was performed as described above. Interestingly Arb displayed an apparent K_D toward peptide Trp between 3.3 and 5.6 μM (Table 4), twice lower than that observed for TOE in PC:chol liposomes. Since both peptides contain one or two tyrosine residues (HCV NS4A and BVDV NS5A, respectively) in addition to the Trp, interaction of Arb molecules with these aromatic residues might account for a higher affinity of Arb for peptides than for a small molecule such as TOE.

Since Arb is an inhibitor of HCV membrane fusion, we reasoned that it might interact with the regions of E1 and E2 described as important for HCV fusion [11,17]. These peptides were described as membranotropic on model membranes [37] and contain aromatic residues. We therefore analyzed the effect of increasing concentrations of Arb on the fluorescence quenching of two peptide sequences derived from HCV E2 (positions 415–432 and 606–625, see aa sequences in Table 5), and inserted into PC:chol liposomes (1:20 peptide-to-lipid molar ratio). Note that we also tested a third peptide located at position 270–283 of E1, containing only one Tyr; but its fluorescence quantum yield was too low to monitor any interpretable fluorescence signal (data not shown). We then calculated the K_D values as described above. As shown in Table 5, E2 415–432 contains only one Trp, whereas E2 606–625 contains one Trp and 3 Tyr. The apparent affinity was in the 15 μM range at pH 7.4 for both peptides, reminiscent to Arb IC50 of HCVpp fusion. This indicates that Arb is able to interact with the aromatic residues of both peptides in the membrane, and lends further support to our hypothesis that Arb could interact with key residues/motifs in viral fusion proteins, which would constitute a possible (partial) explanation to its inhibition of HCVpp fusion. Strikingly this affinity decreased at acidic pH for both peptides, and even drastically to 70 μM for E2 606–625. Interestingly, this relatively high K_D value is reminiscent of that observed for Arb interaction with NATA in solution (Table 3). This suggests that the interaction between the E2 peptide and the membrane would be weak at acidic pH, and that most of the peptide could be in solution. Moreover an histidine residue, located in the immediate vicinity of Trp in the sequence of both peptides, is expected to be charged at pH 5.0. Since Arb is also protonated at that pH value, this could create repulsive forces affecting the interaction between Trp and Arb. Moreover, as protonation of the histidine cycle is expected to decrease the free energy of partition from lipids to water, the peptide could be released from the membrane at acidic pH, possibly in relation with peptide conformational change(s). This behavior in not in favor with their direct role as fusion peptides of HCV, a virus dependent on low pH for its membrane fusion activity. However, due to their membranotropism [37], and since our and other studies showed their involvement in HCV membrane fusion [17,38], it is possible that the conformational changes they might undergo at low pH would lead to a proper relocation of the actual fusion peptide/loop toward the target membrane [39] (and see Discussion section).

Table 4. Apparent dissociation constants between Arb and Trp residues of model membrane-binding peptides inserted into liposomes.

	K_D (µM)[c]	
Membrane peptides[a] inserted in PC:chol liposomes[b]	pH 7.4	pH 5.0
HCV NS4A[1–22]* transmembrane peptide KKGGSTWVLVGGVLAALAAYCLSTGSGGKK	3.3+/-0.6	5.6+/-0.3
BVDV NS5A[1–28] membrane anchor peptide SGNYVLDLIYSLHKQINRGLKKIVLGWA	3.3+/-0.4	4.1+/-0.4

[a]The NMR structures of synthetic peptides HCV NS4A[1–22]* and BVDV NS5A[1–28] peptides have been reported in references [16] and [15], respectively. The solubilization tags KKGG and GGKK at the N- and C-terminal ends, are indicated in italic. Aromatic residues Trp and Tyr are indicated in bold, His is underlined. [b]Peptide-to-lipid molar ratio was 1:20.
[c]K_D values were calculated as described in legend to Figure 7.

Discussion

This study aimed at further investigating the molecular mechanism of action by which arbidol (Arb) inhibits virus cell entry and membrane fusion, using HCVpp as a model of an enveloped virus.
We showed that Arb displayed a dual binding capacity, on lipid membranes interface on one hand and on the aromatic residue tryptophan of proteins on the other hand. It therefore appears plausible that the observed inhibitory effect of Arb on viral entry and membrane fusion might result from a combined effect of binding of Arb on membranes and on (fusion) proteins.

From a physico-chemical point of view, Arb displayed tropism for membranes or membrane-like environments such as detergent micelles, particularly prominent at low pH [12]. By combining several biochemical approaches, we show here that Arb has the propensity to bind to and incorporate into lipid bilayers, with calculated apparent affinities in a similar range as the IC50 value for fusion, i.e. ca. 10 μM. Our NMR studies of Arb interaction with DMPC leads to a model where Arb binds at the membrane interface and establishes contacts mainly with the polar heads of phospholipids (Fig. 5D).

Altogether these data suggest that at least part of Arb inhibitory activity could be explained by its membranotropism. This physico-chemical property has been further emphasized in a recent work by Villalain [40], using Fourier-transform infrared spectroscopy. Arb interaction with phospholipids would disturb membrane fluidity crucial to the fusion process, thereby rendering the lipid bilayer less prone to fusion. Such a model is consistent with the behavior of other indole derivatives, that were shown to exhibit a preference for membrane interfaces [41,42], due to the flat rigid structure of these molecules and to their aromaticity, which allows them to establish cation-p interactions with the positively charged quaternary ammonium lipid headgroups [41,43]. At low pH, the optimal pH for HCV fusion, these interactions would be favored due to the protonation of the amino groups. As was described for other substituted indoles [44], it is possible that protonation of the carbon bearing the ester group of Arb could displace this group out of the indole plane, and place it in a better position to bond with neighboring molecules. This could in turn lead to a better membrane association. Arb might therefore have the propensity to intercalate into lipids of the viral and target membranes while adopting a consistent orientation by filling the gaps between lipid molecules. The interfacial region of the lipid bilayer provides a suitable environment for a wide range of chemical groups, as long as they possess a large enough hydrophobic moiety and a group capable of forming hydrogen bonds with the lipid carbonyl groups. Several compounds with antiviral pharmacological properties belong to this category, in particular adamantanes active against influenza A viruses [45,46] and against some HCV clones but not all [47,48], the natural triterpene glycyrrhizin efficient in the treatment of chronic viral hepatites [49] and the flavonolignan molecules composing silymarin, an herbal extract with potent anti-HCV activities [1–3,50,51].

Table 5. Apparent dissociation constants between Arb and Trp residues of synthetic peptides involved in fusion.

Membrane peptides[a] inserted in PC:chol liposomes[b]	K_D (µM)[c] pH 7.4	K_D (µM)[c] pH 5.0
E2[415–432] NTNGSWHINSTALNCNES	15+/-4	28+/-7
E2[606–625] RCMVDYPYRLWHYPCTI NYT	13+/-3	70+/- 10

[a]Peptides from HCV strain H (genotype 1a, accession number AF009606; [20]). Aromatic residues Trp and Tyr are indicated in bold, His is underlined. [b]Peptide-to-lipid molar ratio was 1:20.
[c]K_D values were calculated as described in legend to Figure 7.

In a previous study, we noticed that Arb inhibition of cell entry concerned HCVpp and pseudoparticles bearing the influenza hemagglutinin (HApp), but not pseudoparticles bearing the envelope glycoprotein of a feline oncogenic retrovirus (Rd114pp) [12]. These data suggest that Arb might display selectivity for the recognition of key motifs inside envelope proteins. This hypothesis was tested by assessing the influence of Arb on the fluorescence properties of aromatic compounds derived from tryptophan (Trp) and of peptides containing Trp. Trp is a component of proteins with interfacial properties [41,42], often located at the lipid/water interface and grouped into so-called tryptophan-rich motifs crucial to protein/membrane association [52], and found in the envelope (fusion) proteins of the SARS coronavirus or HIV-1 [36,53,54]. Trp is also enriched at protein/protein binding interfaces of the small envelope protein of the hepatitis B virus [55] and of membrane proteins in general [56]. We demonstrated here that Arb was able to alter/quench the fluorescence properties of small Trp derivatives in solution (NATA), in detergent micelles and in liposomes (TOE, [57]), in a dose-dependent manner. This occurred most likely through stacking of the aromatic rings of both molecules which is often involved in stabilization of inter-cations. Interestingly the apparent affinity of the Arb/Trp derivative interaction was in the order: lipid bilayers.micelles.solution, indicating that Arb binding strength for Trp could increase in membrane environments where both molecules accomodate and get packed. Indeed Arb apparent affinity for TOE in liposomal membranes was in the 10 μM range, a value comparable to the IC50 of fusion. Arb affinity was even greater for membrane peptides containing Trp and tyrosine (Tyr) residues (ca. 4 μM). Due to its indole group, it is conceivable that Arb might display selectivity not only for indole rings (Trp) but more generally for aromatic groups, as the phenol ring of Tyr. A greater number of Arb molecules could therefore interact with aromatic residues in peptide sequences, leading to some cooperativity in the quenching effect and to an overall larger apparent affinity.
Although HCV entry inhibition by Arb was found genotype-dependent, HCV membrane fusion was inhibited by Arb in a genotype-independent manner. HCV entry and fusion are early steps in the life cycle of the virus [58,59]. HCV first interacts through its envelope glycoproteins with a set of coreceptors at the plasma membrane level (recently reviewed in [60,61]) and eventually becomes endocytosed [62–64]. Due to a combined action of acidification in the endosome and particular lipids like cholesterol and sphingomyelin [11,18], viral fusion occurs over a broad spectrum of pH's ranging from 6.3 to 5.0 [11,18,65]. HCV binding to the hepatocyte membrane followed by endocytosis therefore requires several cellular proteins, and most likely involves several levels of interactions (interactions between viral proteins, between cellular and viral proteins, between viral/cellular proteins and lipids). These features might explain the differential effect exerted by Arb on entry of various HCV genotypes: indeed subtle differences in protein sequences could translate into modified interactions with several partners and/or at several levels. Conversely some common principles of action apply to all fusion reactions, viral fusion and cellular fusion processes alike [66]. Indeed all fusion processes involve two partners: lipids and the fusion protein(s). This might account for the similar inhibitory effect of Arb on HCV fusion observed for all genotypes. This is in line with the observations that Arb displayed potent antiviral activity against some antigenic serotypes of influenza viruses, but not against all [9].

Previously we noticed that Arb inhibition of primary infection of Huh-7.5.1 cells with HCV (clone JFH-1) was efficient only when cells were preincubated with Arb 24 or 48h before infection [10]; in addition, inhibition of HCVpp and HApp cell entry was most efficient when Arb was pre-incubated with both viral and cell membranes [12]. Here, using our in vitro fusion assay, we

observed that Arb inhibition of HCVpp fusion was maximal when both viral and target membranes were incubated with Arb, before fusion was initiated. This suggests that a certain level of membrane impregnation and/or saturation with Arb must be achieved to efficiently inhibit viral infection. Membranes might therefore act as ''concentrators'' of arbidol, and high concentrations of the molecule might be locally achieved. This could explain why Arb, exhibiting an apparent (medium to low) affinity for membranes in the μM range, exerts a relevant antiviral activity without noticeable membrane damages. Along these lines, in spite of its marked membranotropism, Arb displays only low toxicity [9,10]. Arb exhibited a comparable micromolar apparent affinity for aromatic residues present in membrane peptides in a membrane environment. Altogether, these observations lead us to propose a mechanistic model of the way Arb would inhibit HCV entry and fusion. Through its membranotropism, Arb is able to freely interact with viral and target membranes, and could locally get highly concentrated. Arb is also able to interact with aromatic residues within viral proteins involved in membrane interactions and membrane destabilization necessary for fusion. Through this dual binding capacity, Arb could then locally impede the structural rearrangements required for the fusion protein to adopt its fusion conformation. The fact that Arb is active in the μM range suggests that Arb would act by reducing the overall speed of the fusion reaction rather than by blocking a specific protein conformation. This could therefore explain the broad antiviral spectrum of Arb, and the genotype independence of its inhibitory effect on HCV fusion, since HCV envelope proteins contain well-conserved aromatic residues in all genotypes. Mechanistically, the key point is the relative accessibility of these residues to Arb at the membrane interface. A cooperative effect between Arb and several aromatic residues might therefore occur.
Also the local environment of these aromatic aa is important, since the presence of residues such as histidines (His) in their vicinity could modify their accessibility with respect to pH. Interestingly enough, in the sequence of both HCV E2 peptides studied here (Table 5) and shown to be involved in HCV fusion [17], His is contiguous to Trp, and in the 606–625 peptide, His is surrounded by three tyrosines. The concept of His as a critical pH sensor at a key intramolecular domain interface in a viral fusion protein has recently emerged [67,68]. Indeed, the protonation of a sole His in the E protein of the tick-borne encephalitis flavivirus (TBEV) triggers large-scale conformational changes leading to viral fusion. Concerning HCV, Rey and coworkers recently proposed a model of the 3D arrangement of the E2 ectodomain [39]. In this model, the fusion loop/peptide would lie within the poorly structured domain II, and the E2 606–625 peptide would be found in the globally unstructured domain III, where a critical His residue is disposed at the interface with domain I. The putative fusion loop contains a phenylalanine and a tyrosine [39]. At low pH, the optimal pH for HCV membrane fusion, key histidine(s) could become protonated. This could result in conformational rear-rangements and, in the context of Arb fusion inhibition, aromatic residues might consequently become more or less accessible to Arb molecules present in their vicinity. We noted that the apparent affinity of Arb for HCV peptides was weaker at pH 5.0 than at pH 7.4. At low pH, Arb is also protonated, and this protonated form could exhibit a greater preference for the interfacial region of the lipid bilayer than the deprotonated form, as demonstrated for adamantanes [45]. Combined with the notion that key aromatic and His residues would also display interfacial (re)localization at low pH, this would in turn explain the higher efficiency of Arb at inhibiting fusion at acidic pH [12].

In conclusion our data reveal that Arb directly interacts with the lipid membrane-water interface, and is able to bind to aromatic residues present in HCV glycoproteins, in their membrane-associated form. Through a subtle binding interplay between Arb, lipids, viral and cellular proteins, Arb might efficiently block HCV entry and membrane fusion interacting with the main actors of the early steps of viral entry. Most interestingly, Arb inhibition of these processes demonstrated an affinity in the mM range, although the membranotropic properties of Arb suggest that it could become locally more concentrated in membranes. Together, these findings suggest that Arb could increase the strength of viral glycoprotein's interactions with the membrane due to a dual binding mode, involving aromatic residues and phospholipids. The resulting complexation would inhibit the expected viral glycoprotein conformational changes required during the membrane fusion process.

The antiviral mechanism of Arb therefore opens promising perspectives for the development of small membranotropic low affinity molecules, that would become locally concentrated in membranes and would mainly act on the kinetics of the conformational rearrangements of the viral fusion protein.

Supporting Information

Figure S1 Arb inhibits infectivity and membrane fusion in a dose-dependent manner. A, Infectivity. Results are the mean 6 SEM of 5 separate experiments. Black, no Arb; blue, 1.9 μM; green, 5.6 μM and red, 11.3 μM Arb, respectively. B, Membrane fusion between HCVpp of genotype 4 (4.11.21) and R18-labeled liposomes. The lipid mixing kinetic was followed by fluorescence spectroscopy using excitation and emission at 560 and 590 nm, respectively. Fluorescent liposomes (12.5 μM final lipid concentration) were added to 40 μl of HCVpp in PBS pH 7.4 at 37°C, in the absence or presence of the indicated concentrations of Arb. After a 2 min-equilibration, lipid mixing was initiated by decreasing the pH to 5.0 with diluted HCl, and R18 dequenching was recorded. Maximal fluorescence was obtained after addition of 0.1% final Triton X-100. Average value of the last 30 s of fusion (i.e. final extent of fusion) was used to calculate the percentage of fusion in the presence of Arb, relative to 100% fusion without Arb (Figure 2). Black, no Arb; blue, 1.9 μM green, 5.6 μM and red, 11.3 μM Arb, respectively.

Figure S2 NMR of Arbidol into lipid bicelles. A, 1H/13C HSQC spectrum; [Arb]/[lipid] ratio was 1/15 and temperature 305 K. B, extract of 1H NOESY spectrum; [Arb]/[lipid] ratio was 1/10, temperature 290 K and mixing time 200 ms.

Figure S3 Trp emission fluorescence spectrum of a BVDV model peptide into PC:chol liposomes. BVDV NS5A peptide (SGNYVLDLIYSLHKQINRGLKKIVLGWA, 5 mM final) reconstituted into PC:chol liposomes (70:30 molar ratio, peptide-to-lipid ratio 1:20) were equilibrated to 37°C in PBS at pH 7.4 or 5.0 in the absence (thick line) or presence (thin lines) of increasing concentrations of Arb (2, 5, 10, 25 and 100 μM from top to bottom). Trp emission fluorescence was measured between 300 and 400 nm, with excitation at 286 nm. The apparent affinity of Arb toward Trp was calculated from the plot of the difference ΔA between areas under the curve (AUC) of peptide without Arb ($\Delta A = AUC_{no\ Arb} - AUC_{with\ Arb}$) as a function of Arb concentration (insert).

Acknowledgments
This work was presented at the 16th International Symposium on Hepatitis C and related viruses, (Nice, France, October 3–7, 2009). The authors gratefully acknowledge Sylvie Ricard-Blum for SPR analysis expertise. Fluorescence experiments were performed on the platform ''Production et Analyse des Protéines'' of the IFR 128 BioSciences Gerland-Lyon Sud.

Author Contributions
Conceived and designed the experiments: E-IP FP BHM AB. Performed the experiments: ET J-PL DL RM AL GZ. Analyzed the data: ET GZ AL J-PL BHM AB FP E-IP. Contributed reagents/materials/analysis tools: F-LC. Wrote the paper: ET AL FP E-IP.

References

1. Polyak SJ, Morishima C, Lohmann V, Pal S, Lee DY, et al. (2010) Identification of hepatoprotective flavonolignans from silymarin. Proc Natl Acad Sci U S A 107: 5995–5999.
2. Wagoner J, Negash A, Kane OJ, Martinez LE, Nahmias Y, et al. (2010) Multiple effects of silymarin on the hepatitis C virus lifecycle. Hepatology 51: 1912–1921.
3. Ahmed-Belkacem A, Ahnou N, Barbotte L, Wychowski C, Pallier C, et al. (2010) Silibinin and related compounds are direct inhibitors of hepatitis C virus RNA-dependent RNA polymerase. Gastroenterology 138: 1112–1122.
4. Chai H, Zhao Y, Zhao C, Gong P (2006) Synthesis and in vitro anti-hepatitis B virus activities of some ethyl 6-bromo-5-hydroxy-1H-indole-3-carboxylates. Bioorg Med Chem 14: 911–917.
5. Brooks MJ, Sasadeusz JJ, Tannock GA (2004) Antiviral chemotherapeutic agents against respiratory viruses: where are we now and what's in the pipeline? Curr Opin Pulm Med 10: 197–203.
6. Meanwell NA (2006) Hepatitis C virus entry: an intriguing challenge for drug discovery. Curr Opin Investig Drugs 7: 727–732.
7. Yang JP, Zhou D, Wong-Staal F (2009) Screening of small-molecule compounds as inhibitors of HCV entry. Methods Mol Biol 510: 295–304.
8. Leneva IA, Russell RJ, Boriskin YS, Hay AJ (2009) Characteristics of arbidol-resistant mutants of influenza virus: implications for the mechanism of anti-influenza action of arbidol. Antiviral Res 81: 132–140.
9. Boriskin YS, Leneva IA, Pécheur EI, Polyak SJ (2008) Arbidol: a broad-spectrum antiviral compound that blocks viral fusion. Curr Med Chem 15: 997–1005.
10. Boriskin YS, Pécheur EI, Polyak SJ (2006) Arbidol: a broad-spectrum antiviral that inhibits acute and chronic HCV infection. Virol J 3: 56.
11. Haid S, Pietschmann T, Pécheur EI (2009) Low pH-dependent Hepatitis C Virus Membrane Fusion Depends on E2 Integrity, Target Lipid Composition, and Density of Virus Particles. J Biol Chem 284: 17657–17667.
12. Pécheur EI, Lavillette D, Alcaras F, Molle J, Boriskin YS, et al. (2007) Biochemical mechanism of hepatitis C virus inhibition by the broad-spectrum antiviral arbidol. Biochemistry 46: 6050–6059.
13. Sellitto G, Faruolo A, de Caprariis P, Altamura S, Paonessa G, et al. (2010) Synthesis and anti-hepatitis C virus activity of novel ethyl 1H-indole-3-carboxylates in vitro. Bioorg Med Chem 18: 6143–6148.
14. Marcellin P (2009) Hepatitis B and hepatitis C in 2009. Liver Int 29 Suppl 1: 1–8.
15. Sapay N, Montserret R, Chipot C, Brass V, Moradpour D, et al. (2006) NMR structure and molecular dynamics of the in-plane membrane anchor of nonstructural protein 5A from bovine viral diarrhea virus. Biochemistry 45: 2221–2233.
16. Brass V, Berke JM, Montserret R, Blum HE, Penin F, et al. (2008) Structural determinants for membrane association and dynamic organization of the hepatitis C virus NS3-4A complex. Proc Natl Acad Sci U S A 105: 14545–14550.
17. Lavillette D, Pécheur EI, Donot P, Fresquet J, Molle J, et al. (2007) Characterization of fusion determinants points to the involvement of three discrete regions of both E1 and E2 glycoproteins in the membrane fusion process of hepatitis C virus. J Virol 81: 8752–8765.
18. Lavillette D, Bartosch B, Nourrisson D, Verney G, Cosset FL, et al. (2006) Hepatitis C

Virus Glycoproteins Mediate Low pH-dependent Membrane Fusion with Liposomes. J Biol Chem 281: 3909–3917.
19. Nakabayashi H, Taketa K, Miyano K, Yamane T, Sato J (1982) Growth of human hepatoma cells lines with differentiated functions in chemically defined medium. Cancer Res 42: 3858–3863.
20. Lavillette D, Tarr A, Voisset C, Donot P, Bartosch B, et al. (2005) Characterization of host-range and cell entry properties of hepatitis C virus of major genotypes and subtypes. J Virol 41: 265–274.
21. Angelova MI, Hristova N, Tsoneva I (1999) DNA-induced endocytosis upon local microinjection to giant unilamellar cationic vesicles. Eur Biophys J 28: 142–150.
22. Zandomeneghi G, Williamson PT, Hunkeler A, Meier BH (2003) Switched-angle spinning applied to bicelles containing phospholipid-associated peptides. J Biomol NMR 25: 125–132.
23. van Beek JD (2007) matNMR: a flexible toolbox for processing, analyzing and visualizing magnetic resonance data in Matlab. J Magn Reson 187: 19–26.
24. Claessens MM, Leermakers FA, Hoekstra FA, Cohen Stuart MA (2007) Entropic stabilization and equilibrium size of lipid vesicles. Langmuir 23: 6315–6320.
25. Besenicar M, Macek P, Lakey JH, Anderluh G (2006) Surface plasmon resonance in protein-membrane interactions. Chem Phys Lipids 141: 169–178.
26. Ricard-Blum S, Bernocco S, Font B, Moali C, Eichenberger D, et al. (2002) Interaction properties of the procollagen C-proteinase enhancer protein shed light on the mechanism of stimulation of BMP-1. J Biol Chem 277: 33864–33869.
27. Bowles MR, Hall DR, Pond SM, Winzor DJ (1997) Studies of protein interactions by biosensor technology: an alternative approach to the analysis of sensorgrams deviating from pseudo-first-order kinetic behavior. Anal Biochem 244: 133–143.
28. Sanders CR, Hare BJ, Howard KP, Prestegard JH (1994) Magnetically-Oriented Phospholipid Micelles as a Tool for the Study of Membrane-Associated Molecules. Prog Nucl Magn Reson Spectrosc 26: 421–444.
29. Chou JJ, Kaufman JD, Stahl SJ, Wingfield PT, Bax A (2002) Micelle-induced curvature in a water-insoluble HIV-1 Env peptide revealed by NMR dipolar coupling measurement in stretched polyacrylamide gel. J Am Chem Soc 124: 2450–2451.
30. Glover KJ, Whiles JA, Wu G, Yu N, Deems R, et al. (2001) Structural evaluation of phospholipid bicelles for solution-state studies of membrane-associated biomolecules. Biophys J 81: 2163–2171.
31. Vold RR, Prosser RS, Deese AJ (1997) Isotropic solutions of phospholipid bicelles: a new membrane mimetic for high-resolution NMR studies of polypeptides. J Biomol NMR 9: 329–335.
32. Pintacuda G, Otting G (2002) Identification of protein surfaces by NMR measurements with a pramagnetic Gd(III) chelate. J Am Chem Soc 124: 372–373.
33. Respondek M, Madl T, Gobl C, Golser R, Zangger K (2007) Mapping the orientation of helices in micelle-bound peptides by paramagnetic relaxation waves. J Am Chem Soc 129: 5228–5234.
34. Zangger K, Respondek M, Gobl C, Hohlweg W, Rasmussen K, et al. (2009) Positioning of micelle-bound peptides by paramagnetic relaxation enhance-ments. J Phys Chem B 113: 4400–4406.
35. Bertini I, Luchinat C (1996) NMR of Paramagnetic substances. Coor Chem Rev.

36. Kliger Y, Peisajovich SG, Blumenthal R, Shai Y (2000) Membrane-induced conformational change during the activation of HIV-1 gp41. J Mol Biol 301: 905–914.
37. Perez-Berna AJ, Moreno MR, Guillen J, Bernabeu A, Villalain J (2006) The membrane-active regions of the hepatitis C virus E1 and E2 envelope glycoproteins. Biochemistry 45: 3755–3768.
38. Drummer HE, Boo I, Poumbourios P (2007) Mutagenesis of a conserved fusion peptide-like motif and membrane-proximal heptad-repeat region of hepatitis C virus glycoprotein E1. J Gen Virol 88: 1144–1148.
39. Krey T, d'Alayer J, Kikuti CM, Saulnier A, Damier-Piolle L, et al. (2010) The disulfide bonds in glycoprotein E2 of hepatitis C virus reveal the tertiary organization of the molecule. PLoS Pathog 6: e1000762.
40. Villalain J (2010) Membranotropic effects of arbidol, a broad anti-viral molecule, on phospholipid model membranes. J Phys Chem B 114: 8544–8554.
41. Petersen FN, Jensen MO, Nielsen CH (2005) Interfacial tryptophan residues: a role for the cation-pi effect? Biophys J 89: 3985–3996.
42. Yau WM, Wimley WC, Gawrisch K, White SH (1998) The preference of tryptophan for membrane interfaces. Biochemistry 37: 14713–14718.
43. Zacharias N, Dougherty DA (2002) Cation-pi interactions in ligand recognition and catalysis. Trends Pharmacol Sci 23: 281–287.
44. Hinman RL, Lang J (1964) The Protonation of Indoles. Basicity Studies. The Dependence of Acidity Functions on Indicator Structure. Journal of the American Chemical Society 86: 3796–3806.
45. Chew CF, Guy A, Biggin PC (2008) Distribution and dynamics of adamantanes in a lipid bilayer. Biophys J 95: 5627–5636.
46. Cady SD, Schmidt-Rohr K, Wang J, Soto CS, Degrado WF, et al. (2010) Structure of the amantadine binding site of influenza M2 proton channels in lipid bilayers. Nature 463: 689–692.
47. Griffin SD, Beales LP, Clarke DS, Worsfold O, Evans SD, et al. (2003) The p7 protein of hepatitis C virus forms an ion channel that is blocked by the antiviral drug, Amantadine. FEBS Lett 535: 34–38.
48. Montserret R, Saint N, Vanbelle C, Salvay AG, Simorre JP, et al. (2010) NMR structure and ion channel activity of the p7 protein from hepatitis C virus. J Biol Chem.
49. Schrofelbauer B, Raffetseder J, Hauner M, Wolkerstorfer A, Ernst W, et al. (2009) Glycyrrhizin, the main active compound in liquorice, attenuates pro-inflammatory responses by interfering with membrane-dependent receptor signalling. Biochem J 421: 473–482.
50. Chaudhuri S, Pahari B, Sengupta PK (2009) Ground and excited state proton transfer and antioxidant activity of 7-hydroxyflavone in model membranes: absorption and fluorescence spectroscopic studies. Biophys Chem 139: 29–36.
51. Chaudhuri S, Basu K, Sengupta B, Banerjee A, Sengupta PK (2008) Ground-and excited-state proton transfer and antioxidant activity of 3-hydroxyflavone in egg yolk phosphatidylcholine liposomes: absorption and fluorescence spectro-scopic studies. Luminescence 23: 397–403.
52. Gruber A, Cornaciu I, Lass A, Schweiger M, Poeschl M, et al. (2010) The N-terminal region of comparative gene identification-58 (CGI-58) is important for lipid droplet binding and activation of adipose triglyceride lipase. J Biol Chem
285:12289–12298.

53. Salzwedel K, West JT, Hunter E (1999) A conserved tryptophan-rich motif in the membrane-proximal region of the human immunodeficiency virus type 1 gp41 ectodomain is important for Env-mediated fusion and virus infectivity. J Virol 73: 2469–2480.
54. Broer R, Boson B, Spaan W, Cosset FL, Corver J (2006) Important role for the transmembrane domain of severe acute respiratory syndrome coronavirus spike protein during entry. J Virol 80: 1302–1310.
55. Komla-Soukha I, Sureau C (2006) A tryptophan-rich motif in the carboxyl terminus of the small envelope protein of hepatitis B virus is central to the assembly of hepatitis delta virus particles. J Virol 80: 4648–4655.
56. Granseth E, von Heijne G, Elofsson A (2005) A study of the membrane-water interface region of membrane proteins. J Mol Biol 346: 377–385.
57. de Foresta B, Gallay J, Sopkova J, Champeil P, Vincent M (1999) Tryptophan octyl ester in detergent micelles of dodecylmaltoside: fluorescence properties and quenching by brominated detergent analogs. Biophys J 77: 3071–3084.
58. Moradpour D, Penin F, Rice CM (2007) Replication of Hepatitis C virus. Nature Rev Microbiol 5: 453–463.
59. von Hahn T, Rice CM (2008) Hepatitis C virus entry. J Biol Chem 283: 3689–3693.
60. Perrault M, Pécheur EI (2009) The hepatitis C virus and its hepatic environment: a toxic but finely tuned partnership. Biochem J 423: 303–314.
61. Pietschmann T (2009) Virology: Final entry key for hepatitis C. Nature 457: 797–798.
62. Tscherne DM, Jones CT, Evans MJ, Lindenbach BD, McKeating JA, et al. (2006) Time- and temperature-dependent activation of hepatitis C virus for low-pH-triggered entry. J Virol 80: 1734–1741.
63. Meertens L, Bertaux C, Dragic T (2006) Hepatitis C virus entry requires a critical postinternalization step and delivery to early endosomes via clathrin-coated vesicles. J Virol 80: 11571–11578.
64. Coller KE, Berger KL, Heaton NS, Cooper JD, Yoon R, et al. (2009) RNA interference and single particle tracking analysis of hepatitis C virus endocytosis. PLoS Pathog 5: e1000702.
65. Kobayashi M, Bennett MC, Bercot T, Singh IR (2006) Functional analysis of hepatitis C virus envelope proteins, using a cell-cell fusion assay. J Virol 80: 1817–1825.
66. Sapir A, Avinoam O, Podbilewicz B, Chernomordik LV (2008) Viral and developmental cell fusion mechanisms: conservation and divergence. Dev Cell 14: 11–21.
67. Fritz R, Stiasny K, Heinz FX (2008) Identification of specific histidines as pH sensors in flavivirus membrane fusion. J Cell Biol 183: 353–361.
68. Harrison SC (2008) The pH sensor for flavivirus membrane fusion. J Cell Biol 183: 177-179.
69. Schwieters CD, Kuszewski JJ, Tjandra N, Clore GM (2003) The Xplor-NIH NMR molecular structure determination package. J Magn Reson 160: 65–73.

La molécule antivirale arbidol inhibe des virus pathogènes de prévalence mondiale

Ève-Isabelle Pécheur[1], Stephen J. Polyak[2]

[1] Université de Lyon, Université Claude Bernard Lyon 1, Inserm 1052, CNRS 5286, Centre de Recherche en Cancérologie de Lyon, 151, cours Albert Thomas, 69003 Lyon, France.
[2] Departments of Laboratory Medicine and Global Health, University of Washington, Seattle, Washington, États-Unis. eve-isabelle.pecheur@inserm.fr

À l'heure actuelle, il reste de nombreux virus de prévalence mondiale contre les-quels il n'existe ni traitement antiviral, ni vaccin. Certains de ces virus, comme le virus Ebola[1] ou les membres du genre des Arenavirus[2], à l'origine d'infections aiguës, causent des maladies hémorragiques sévères pouvant être fatales. D'autres, comme le virus de l'hépatite B (VHB) ou certains herpès virus, établissent des infections persistantes pouvant évoluer en maladies chroniques, dont le cancer. Afin de contrer ces virus, il apparaît donc nécessaire de pouvoir identifier une molécule à action antivirale qui soit abordable, efficace et sûre. L'arbidol, un antiviral qui est déjà utilisé en clinique dans plusieurs pays comme traitement anti-grippal, pourrait être un candidat.

L'arbidol : un agent antiviral à large spectre

L'arbidol a été initialement synthétisé dans les années 1970, en URSS[3] (voir *Figure 1A* pour sa structure chimique). Il y est commercialisé depuis plus de 20 ans pour la prophylaxie et le traitement de maladies pulmonaires humaines dues aux virus A et B de la grippe, ainsi que d'autres virus respiratoires pathogènes [1, 2]. Il est également utilisé en cli-nique en Chine depuis 2006 pour les mêmes indications ainsi que pour la prévention d'épidémies de grippe aviaire en médecine vétérinaire [3]. Son inno-cuité a été démontrée sur des périodes de traitement allant d'une semaine à quelques mois.

Des études récentes ont montré l'efficacité de l'arbidol *in vivo* contre des virus responsables d'infections respiratoires (virus respiratoire syncytial, virus Cox-sackie B5) ou contre le virus Hantaan qui cause une fièvre hémorragique accom-pagnée d'un syndrome rénal d'issue sou-vent fatale [3]. Ces études ayant été effectuées sur un petit nombre d'animaux, leur interprétation doit cependant rester prudente.

[1] Le virus Ebola appartient à la famille des *Filoviridae*, comprenant également le virus Marburg. Ce sont des virus à ARN simple brin de polarité négative, causant tous deux des fièvres hémorragiques. Plusieurs espèces de virus Ebola existent : Forêt Taï, Soudan, Zaïre, Reston et Bundidugyo.

[2] Les Arenavirus sont un genre viral appartenant à la famille des *Arenaviridae*, comprenant notamment le virus de la fièvre de Lassa, les virus Tacaribe, Junin, Machupo, Guanarito, Sabia, Lujo et Chapare (virus du Nouveau Monde) et le virus de la chorioménin-gite lymphocytaire (virus de l'Ancien Monde). Les réservoirs sont la chauve-souris pour Tacaribe, et les rongeurs pour les autres virus. Tous ces virus sont responsables de fièvres hémorragiques parfois létale.

[3] Union des républiques socialistes soviétiques ou Union soviétique.

Une étude récente fait en effet état d'une absence d'activité antivirale, à la dose utilisée *in vivo*, contre le virus de la fièvre hémorragique Crimée-Congo[4]. La réplication de ce virus est toutefois inhibée par l'arbidol *in vitro* [4]. Le spectre antiviral de l'arbidol *in vitro* s'élargit donc à des pathogènes émergents comme le coro-navirus causant le syndrome respiratoire aigu sévère (SRAS), le virus Chikungunya, ainsi qu'aux virus des hépatites virales B et C [3]. Ces virus sont différents d'un point de vue structural (virus enveloppés ou non, à ADN ou ARN) et leurs cycles réplicatifs sont différents. Nous avons émis l'hypothèse que l'arbidol pourrait présenter une activité antivirale contre d'autres pathogènes, comme certains Arenavirus ou le virus Ebola, responsable de l'épidémie récente qui a touché plus de 28000 personnes et est à l'origine de 11000 décès[5], et que son action pourrait cibler les particules virales et/ou la cellule infectée, en bloquant une(des) voie(s) intracellulaire(s) utilisée(s) par l'ensemble de ces virus au cours de leur cycle infectieux.

L'arbidol inhibe l'infection par des virus de prévalence mondiale

Nous avons étudié l'arbidol dans un programme de test antiviral *in vitro* de l'institut « Allergie et Maladies infectieuses » du NIH (NIAID, *National institute of allergy and infectious diseases* ; NIH, *National institutes of health*). Nous avons ainsi identifié une activité inhibitrice de l'arbidol pour les infections par l'Arenavirus Tacaribe, ainsi que par les herpès virus HHV-8 (herpèsvirus humain type 8), VHB et Ebola souche Zaïre [5]. Cette inhibition a été observée pour des doses efficaces bloquant 50 % de l'infection (CE_{50}) variant de 1 à 6 µM, sauf pour VHB où la CE_{50} était de l'ordre de 20 µM. Ces doses sont comparables aux concentrations mesurées dans le plasma de sujets sains ayant reçu par voie orale une dose d'ar-bidol susceptible d'être administrée à des patients présentant un état grippal [3]. En outre, les index de sélectivité[6] mesurés *in vitro* variaient entre 6 et 40, ce qui indique une faible cytotoxi-cité de cette molécule. Dans l'infection par HHV-8, l'arbidol a démontré une efficacité antivirale équivalente à la molécule de référence, le cidofovir [5]. Concernant les virus Ebola et Tacaribe, responsables de fièvres hémorragiques létales et contre lesquels n'existe à ce jour aucun antiviral ni vaccin, l'arbidol pourrait constituer un espoir de lutte contre ces infections.

L'arbidol inhibe les étapes précoces de l'infection par le virus Ebola

Pour le virus Ebola souche Zaïre, nous avons approfondi nos études et réalisé des expériences de temps d'addition. L'arbidol est ajouté aux cellules avant infection, ou au moment de l'inocula-tion virale, ou à différents temps post-infection. Nous avons ainsi observé que l'action antivirale de l'arbidol s'exerçait de manière optimale quand la molécule était mise en contact avec les cellules avant l'inoculum viral [5] *(Figure 1B)*.

[4] Le virus de la fièvre hémorragique de Crimée-Congo provoque des flambées de fièvre hémorragique virale sévère avec un taux de létalité pouvant atteindre 40 %.

[5] http://apps.who.int/iris/bitstream/10665/ 208883/1/ebolasitrep_10Jun2016_eng.pdf?ua=1

[6] L'index de sélectivité caractérise l'innocuité d'une molécule. Il est défini comme le rapport entre la concentration causant 50% de cytotoxicité (CC_{50}) et la concentration bloquant 50% de l'infection (CE_{50}) : $IS = CC_{50}/CE_{50}$. Plus cet index est élevé, moins la molécule présente de danger à l'administration.

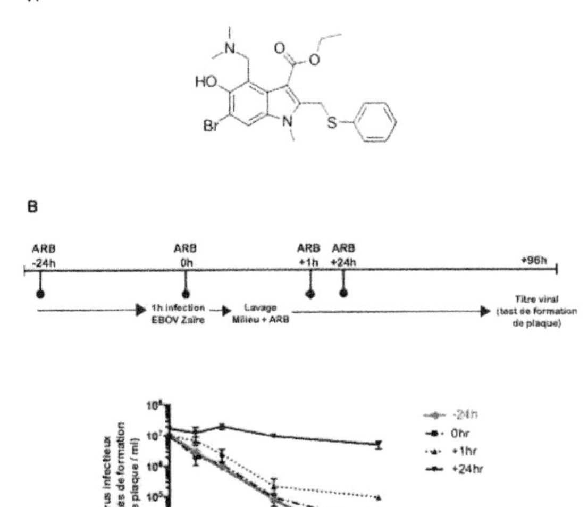

Figure 1. L'arbidol inhibe un stade précoce du cycle infectieux du virus Ebola. A. Structure chimique de l'arbidol. ***B.*** Les hépatocytes HepG2 sont traités avec 0, 2,35, 4,7, 9,4 ou 18,8 µM d'arbidol (ARB) pendant 24 h avant infection (- 24 h), au moment de l'infection (0 h), 1 h (+ 1 h) ou 24 h (+ 24 h) après l'infection. Les cellules sont infectées avec le virus Ebola (EBOV) souche Zaïre pendant 1 h, puis du milieu frais contenant de l'arbidol est ajouté aux cultures. Un test de formation de plaques est effectué au bout de 96h d'infection, pour évaluer le titre viral.

Cette observation suggérait que les étapes précoces de l'infection étaient ciblées par l'arbidol, c'est-à-dire les étapes de l'entrée virale (attachement des virions aux cellules, internalisa-tion en compartiments intracellulaires, fusion membranaire). Pour affiner nos données, nous avons utilisé un modèle de pseudoparticules virales exprimant la glycoprotéine d'enveloppe du virus Ebola à leur surface. Ce modèle est bien adapté à l'étude de l'entrée virale, car, après leur internalisation intra-cellulaire, ces particules sont dépour-vues de capacités réplicatives. Nous avons ainsi pu confirmer que l'arbidol ciblait l'entrée du virus Ebola dans ses cellules-hôte.

Mécanisme d'action antivirale de l'arbidol

Du fait de son large spectre antiviral, deux hypothèses plausibles de mécanisme se dégagent pour expliquer l'effet inhibiteur de l'arbidol : (1) l'arbidol agirait sur les lipides et/ou les protéines composant les particules virales ; (2) l'arbidol agirait sur des cibles cellulaires. Ces hypothèses n'étant pas mutuellement exclusives, ceci rangerait l'arbidol dans la classe des agents anti-viraux à action directe (*direct antiviral agents*, DAA) et/ou des agents ciblant l'hôte (*host targeting agents*, HTA).

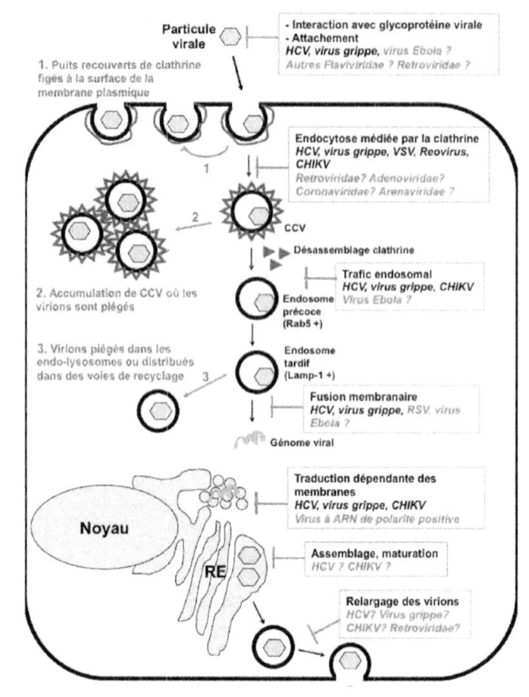

Figure 2. L'activité à large spectre de l'arbidol et ses mécanismes d'action moléculaire au niveau cellulaire. Les différentes étapes du cycle viral inhibées par l'arbidol sont indiquées dans des boîtes bleues. Les virus sur lesquels l'effet de l'arbidol est attesté sont indiqués en noir, l'effet potentiel de l'arbidol sur d'autres virus ou familles de virus est mentionné en rouge. Les flèches bleues et le texte indiquent les conséquences de l'effet de l'arbidol sur les voies cellulaires et les virions. Pour la clarté de la figure, et d'après les connaissances actuelles des mécanismes moléculaires d'action de l'arbidol, seule la voie de l'endocytose dépendante de la clathrine est montrée. VHC : virus de l'hépatite C ; VSV : virus de la stomatite vésiculaire ; CHIKV : virus Chikungunya ; RSV : virus respiratoire syncytial ; CCV : vésicule recouverte de clathrine ; RE : réticulum endoplasmique ; Lamp-1 : *lysosomal-associated membrane protein 1* (droit de reproduction d'après [3], © n° de licence 3906600433506 du 12-07-2016).

Nos études biochimiques, combinant des approches de RMN (résonance magnétique nucléaire) du solide, de spectroscopie de fluorescence, de résonance plasmonique de surface[7] et d'imagerie, ont révélé que l'arbidol s'insère dans les membranes lipidiques artificielles (liposomes) et les rigidifie. Cette insertion se réalise d'autant mieux que le pH est acide, et avec une affinité de l'ordre du µM [6], réminiscente de la CE_{50} antivirale. L'arbidol montre également une affinité du même ordre pour les acides aminés aromatiques présents au sein d'une séquence polypeptidique. Ces acides aminés aromatiques sont notamment présents dans des régions de l'hémagglutinine de l'enveloppe du virus de la grippe ou de la glycoprotéine E2 de l'enveloppe du virus de l'hépatite C (VHC) [3, 6], régions impliquées dans l'entrée cellulaire et la fusion membranaire de ces deux virus. Ce mode d'action double, par incorporation dans les membranes d'une part (membrane virale dans ce cas), et par interaction avec les régions de protéines virales responsables de l'entrée et de la fusion virale d'autre part, rangerait l'arbidol dans la classe des DAA. L'hypothèse d'une action de type HTA a été testée dans le contexte de l'infection par VHC. Ce virus est internalisé dans ses cellules-cible, les hépatocytes, par endocytose dépendante de la clathrine [7, 8] .

[7] La résonance plasmonique de surface est un phénomène physique sur lequel repose la mesure de la liaison d'un « ligand » sur un « récepteur » adsorbé à la surface d'une couche métallique (biocapteur ou *sensor chip*). L'application consiste à déposer sur l'interface une couche d'or riche en électrons libres, recouverte éventuellement de revêtements appropriés à la fixation de « récepteurs » de nature protéique, glycosidique, lipidique, etc. Le « ligand » dilué dans un tampon circule à flux constant à la surface du biocapteur. Un faisceau de lumière incident riche en photons est dirigé sur le biocapteur, et ces photons incidents peuvent alors entrer en résonance avec des électrons libres. Les changements de masse induits par l'association ou dissociation des complexes modifient la réfringence du milieu et décalent la position de l'angle de résonance. L'enregistrement de la variation de l'angle de réso-nance permet ainsi de suivre en temps réel la fixation des molécules injectées sur le biocapteur.

La libération de son matériel génétique a ensuite lieu après abaissement du pH dans les endosomes et fusion des membranes virale et endosomale [9] *(Figure* 2). Nous avons montré que l'arbidol ralentissait l'endocytose des virions VHC et inhibait la fixation de la petite GTPase Rab5 sur les endosomes impliqués dans le trafic des virions [10, 11] . Ceci a pour effet de différer le moment auquel prend place la fusion virale ; les virions, n'ayant pas pu libérer leur nucléocapside, seraient alors dirigés vers des compartiments de dégrada-tion de type lysosome [10]. L'arbidol inhibe également la scission membra-naire induite par la dynamine-2, ce qui altère la formation des vésicules recou-vertes de clathrine et donc l'endocytose dépendante de la clathrine.
Dans l'état actuel de la littérature, l'arbidol montre une activité antivirale contre des virus pénétrant dans leurs cellules-hôte par des voies utilisant soit une acidification, soit l'action de la GTPase Rab5, soit l'action de la dynamine-2. L'internalisation du virus Ebola requiert une étape d'acidification endosomale, ainsi que l'intervention des petites GTPases Rab5 et Rab7 [12]. Cette étape et ces protéines pourraient donc être ciblées par l'arbidol, ce qui expliquerait l'inhibition observée sur les étapes précoces de l'entrée du virus Ebola *(Figure* 2).
Étant donné que l'arbidol semble être le plus efficace lorsqu'il est administré avant ou au moment de la survenue de l'infection par le virus Ebola, et du fait de son innocuité démontrée en cli-nique, il pourrait être utilisé en pro-phylaxie dans les épidémies de fièvres hémorragiques, en limitant la dissé-mination virale chez les personnes en contact avec les malades (famille, per-sonnel prodiguant les soins, etc.). Chez les patients infectés, l'administration d'arbidol pourrait permettre de circonscrire ou d'atténuer les symptômes de l'infection, en protégeant les cellules non infectées.
Des recherches futures en ce sens pour-raient donner l'espoir d'un traitement efficace et rapide à mettre en œuvre contre ces infections redoutables. ‡

LIENS D'INTÉRÊT

Les auteurs déclarent n'avoir aucun lien d'intérêt concernant les données publiées dans cet article.

RÉFÉRENCES

1. Boriskin YS, Leneva IA, Pécheur EI, Polyak SJ. Arbidol: a broad-spectrum antiviral compound that blocks viral fusion. *Curr Med Chem* 2008 ; 15 : 997-1005.
2. Brooks MJ, Sasadeusz JJ, Tannock GA. Antiviral chemotherapeutic agents against respiratory viruses: where are we now and what's in the pipeline? *Curr Opin Pulm Med* 2004 ; 10 : 197-203.
3. Blaising J, Polyak SJ, Pécheur EI. Arbidol as a broad-spectrum antiviral: an update. *Antiviral Res* 2014 ; 107 : 84-94.
4. Oestereich L, Rieger T, Neumann M, *et al.* Evaluation of antiviral efficacy of ribavirin, arbidol, and T-705 (favipiravir) in a mouse model for Crimean-Congo hemorrhagic fever. *PLoS Negl Trop Dis* 2014 ; 8 : e2804.
5. Pécheur EI, Borisevich V, Halfmann P, *et al.* The synthetic antiviral drug arbidol inhibits globally prevalent pathogenic viruses. *J Virol* 2016 ; 90 : 3086-92.
6. Teissier E, Zandomeneghi G, Loquet A, *et al.* Mechanism of inhibition of enveloped virus membrane fusion by the antiviral drug arbidol. *PLoS One* 2011 ; 6 : e15874.
7. Coller KE, Berger KL, Heaton NS, *et al.* RNA interference and single particle tracking analysis of hepatitis C virus endocytosis. *PLoS Pathog* 2009 ; 5 : e1000702.
8. Boucrot E, McMahon HT. Initiation de l'endocytose par vésicules de clathrine : des « sculpteurs de membrane » au travail. *Med Sci (Paris)* 2011 ; 27 : 122-5.
9. Blaising J, Lévy PL, Gondeau C, *et al.* Silibinin inhibits hepatitis C virus entry into hepatocytes by hindering clathrin-dependent trafficking. *Cell Microbiol* 2013 ; 15 : 1866-82.
10. Blaising J, Lévy PL, Polyak SJ, *et al.* Arbidol inhibits viral entry by interfering with clathrin-dependent trafficking. *Antiviral Res* 2013 ; 100 : 215-9.
11. Gilleron J, Zeigerer A, Marsico G, *et al.* Rôle clé de la petite GTPase Rab5 : de la biogenèse des endosomes au métabolisme du foie. *Med Sci (Paris)* 2012 ; 28 : 1041-4.
12. Spence JS, Krause TB, Mittler E, *et al.* Direct visualization of Ebola virus fusion triggering in the endocytic pathway. *MBio* 2016 ; 7 : e01857-15.

The Synthetic Antiviral Drug Arbidol Inhibits Globally Prevalent Pathogenic Viruses

Eve-Isabelle Pécheur,[a] Viktoriya Borisevich,[b] Peter Halfmann,[c] John D. Morrey,[d] Donald F. Smee,[d] Mark Prichard,[e] Chad E. Mire,[b] Yoshihiro Kawaoka,[c,f] Thomas W. Geisbert,[b] Stephen J. Polyak[g,h]

CRCL, Inserm U1052, CNRS 5286, University of Lyon, Lyon, France[a]; Galveston National Laboratory, Department of Microbiology and Immunology, University of Texas Medical Branch, Galveston, Texas, USA[b]; Department of Pathobiological Sciences, University of Wisconsin, Madison, Wisconsin, USA[c]; Institute for Antiviral Research, Utah State University, Logan, Utah, USA[d]; Department of Pediatrics, University of Alabama School of Medicine, Birmingham, Alabama, USA[e]; International Research Center for Infectious Diseases and Division of Virology, Department of Microbiology and Immunology, Institute of Medical Science, University of Tokyo, Tokyo, Japan[f]; Departments of Laboratory Medicine[g] and Global Health,[h] University of Washington, Seattle, Washington, USA

ABSTRACT

Arbidol (ARB) is a synthetic antiviral originally developed to combat influenza viruses. ARB is currently used clinically in several countries but not in North America. We have previously shown that ARB inhibits *in vitro* hepatitis C virus (HCV) by blocking HCV entry and replication. In this report, we expand the list of viruses that are inhibited by ARB and demonstrate that ARB suppresses *in vitro* infection of mammalian cells with Ebola virus (EBOV), Tacaribe arenavirus, and human herpesvirus 8 (HHV-8). We also confirm suppression of hepatitis B virus and poliovirus by ARB. ARB inhibited EBOV Zaire Kikwit infection when added before or at the same time as virus infection and was less effective when added 24h after EBOV infection. Experiments with recombinant vesicular stomatitis virus (VSV) expressing the EBOV Zaire glycoprotein showed that infection was inhibited by ARB at early stages, most likely at the level of viral entry into host cells. ARB inhibited HHV-8 replication to a similar degree as cidofovir. Our data broaden the spectrum of antiviral efficacy of ARB to include globally prevalent viruses that cause significant morbidity and mortality.

IMPORTANCE

There are many globally prevalent viruses for which there are no licensed vaccines or antiviral medicines. Some of these viruses, such as Ebola virus or members of the arenavirus family, rapidly cause severe hemorrhagic diseases that can be fatal. Other viruses, such as hepatitis B virus or human herpesvirus 8 (HHV-8), establish persistent infections that cause chronic illnesses, including cancer. Thus, finding an affordable, effective, and safe drug that blocks many viruses remains an unmet medical need. The antiviral drug arbidol (ARB), already in clinical use in several countries as an anti-influenza treatment, has been previously shown to suppress the growth of many viruses. In this report, we expand the list of viruses that are blocked by ARB in a laboratory setting to include Ebola virus, Tacaribe arenavirus, and HHV-8, and we propose ARB as a broad-spectrum antiviral drug that may be useful against hemorrhagic viruses.

The past several decades have witnessed significant advances in the control of globally prevalent viral infections, with hepatitis C virus (HCV) as the most recent example (1). Nonetheless, even with successful vaccines and therapies for some of these patho-gens, viral mutation, drug resistance, and viral reemergence pose problems for global control and eradication efforts. Even more distressing is the recent outbreak of the filovirus Ebola virus (EBOV), affecting multiple countries in West Africa (2) and in-cluding two imported into cases the United States (with one death) and two locally acquired infections in U.S. health care workers. Other than supportive care and hydration therapy, there currently exist no treatments, licensed vaccines, or antiviral drugs for acute EBOV infection. Moreover, there are no prophylactic treatments that could reduce spread during an outbreak and protect health care workers who treat an EBOV-infected patient.

There are other gaps in the armamentarium against global viral infections. For example, arenaviruses represent a family of am-bisense RNA viruses capable of causing fatal hemorrhagic dis-eases, such as Lassa fever (3). Tacaribe arenavirus can also cause febrile illness (4). There exist few effective therapies for human herpesvirus 8 (HHV-8), the causative agent of Kaposi's sarcoma (5). Poliovirus still shows clusters of reemergence in several coun-tries, including Pakistan, Afghanistan, and Nigeria (6). Viral hepatitis, caused by chronic hepatitis B virus (HBV) and hepatitis C virus (HCV) infection, affects over 350 million people worldwide and is the fifth leading cause of cancer, killing nearly 1 million people annually (7).

There is a growing appreciation that arbidol (ARB) {ethyl 6-bromo-4-[(dimethylamino)methyl]-5-hydroxy-1-methyl-2-(phenylsulfanylmethyl)indole-3-carboxylate;hydrate; hydrochloride} has broad-spectrum antiviral activity. ARB was developed in Russia to combat influenza virus (8) and has been in clinical use in Russia and China for decades (9). Since then, ARB has been shown to inhibit the replication of multiple virus

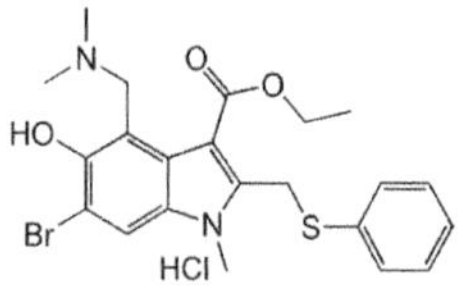

FIG 1 Structure of ARB, ethyl 6-bromo-4-[(dimethylamino)methyl]-5-hydroxy-1-methyl-2-(phenylsulfanylmethyl)indole-3-carboxylate;hydrate; hydrochloride (PubChem compound 131410).

families that exert clinical impacts globally. ARB inhibits mem-bers of the families *Orthomyxoviridae*, *Paramyxoviridae*, and *Pi-cornaviridae* (10), *Bunyaviridae*, *Rhabdoviridae*, *Reoviridae*, *Toga-viridae*, and *Hepadnaviridae* (11), and *Hepaciviridae* (12). In this report, we demonstrate for the first time the antiviral potential of ARB against Ebola virus (EBOV), arenaviruses (Tacaribe virus), and herpesviruses (HHV-8). We also confirm ARB antiviral activ-ity against poliovirus and HBV.

MATERIALS AND METHODS

Starting material. ARB (Fig. 1) was synthesized commercially and provided by Gary Rohrabaugh of Good Earth Medicine, LLC. The University of Washington Mass Spectrometry Center evaluated our stocks of ARB by nuclear magnetic resonance spectroscopy and mass spectrometry and confirmed that they are 99% pure and identical to the original 1970 formulation (data not shown). ARB was dissolved in dimethyl sulfoxide (DMSO) for all *in vitro* tests except for testing against EBOV, where ARB was solubilized in ethanol.

Cells and viruses. For *in vitro* testing of HHV-8, Tacaribe virus, po-liovirus, and HBV, the University of Washington utilized the nonclinical and preclinical services program offered by the National Institute of Al-lergy and Infectious Diseases (NIAID). For HHV-8, BCBL-1 cells were induced to undergo lytic replication by the addition of 100 ng/ml phorbol 12-myristate 13-acetate (Promega, Madison, WI). One hour later, activated cells were seeded in 96-well plates containing 5-fold dilutions of ARB. The replicated DNA was then isolated and quantified by quantitative PCR (qPCR) using methods reported previously (13). HBV (strain ayw) replication was tested in HepG2 2.2.1 cells, which constitutively replicate the HBV genome (14). HBV replication was quantified using PCR as described previously (15). Tacaribe virus (strain TRVL11573) and poliovirus type 3 (strain WM-3) were tested in Vero cells by viral cyto-pathic effect inhibition assays using neutral red uptake as an indicator of cell viability (16, 17). ARB was added 10 min prior to infection with Tacaribe virus or poliovirus at a multiplicity of infection (MOI) of 0.001.

For EBOV infection, HepG2 cells were seeded at 2 10^5 cells per well in 12-well plates the day prior to infection. Cells were then infected with EBOV strain Zaire Kikwit at an MOI of 0.5 for 1 h at 37°C. The inoculum was removed, and the cells were washed with phosphate-buffered saline (PBS) four times. ARB was dissolved in 96% ethanol to create a 10-mg/ml stock, and ultrapure water was then added to make a final stock of 1 mg/ml. Working dilutions were made in complete minimal essential medium (MEM). ARB treatments included adding ARB 24h before infection, at the same time as viral adsorption, 1h after virus infection, and 24h postinfection. Medium containing the indicated concentrations of ARB was always added after the appropriate pretreatment and virus adsorption period. Supernatants were harvested at 96h postinfection and diluted in most instances at least 100-fold prior to titration on Vero E6 cells. This dilution step reduced the concentration of carryover ARB to less than 0.1 μg/ml, which does not inhibit EBOV. Thus, the resultant titer data are reflective of ARB suppression of EBOV replication in HepG2 cells as opposed to carryover ARB suppression of EBOV in Vero E6 cells during viral titer determination.

For experiments with vesicular stomatitis virus (VSV), Vero cells, seeded at 200,000 cells per well, were treated with vehicle or 10 μM ARB for 1h before infection, at the time of infection, or 1 h after infection. Cells were infected with wild-type VSV or recombinant VSV expressing the Zaire Ebola virus glycoprotein (VSV-EbGP) at an MOI of 0.001. After an infection of 1 h, cells were washed 4 times to remove unbound virus, and medium with vehicle or 10 μM ARB was added back to cells. Twenty-four hours after infection, cell culture supernatants were harvested, and virus titers were determined by standard plaque assay on Vero cells.

Cytotoxicity of ARB on HepG2 cells was evaluated by measuring cel-lular ATP levels with a commercial kit (ATPlite assay; PerkinElmer).

Data analysis. The effective concentration of compound that sup-presses viral replication by 50% (EC_{50}) and concentration of compound that causes 50% cytotoxicity (CC_{50}) were calculated with PRISM 4.0 (GraphPad, USA) using a built-in 4-parametric sigmoid function with variable slope. The ratio of antiviral EC_{50} to CC_{50} was used to calculate a selectivity index (SI) (CC_{50}/EC_{50}). *t* tests were performed to compare differences between controls and doses of ARB.

RESULTS

ARB inhibits the early stages of Ebola virus infection. The CC_{50} for ARB (Fig. 1) in HepG2 cells was 24.36 +/- 0.55 μM (Fig. 2A). HepG2 cells were pretreated for 24 h with 0 to 18.8 μM ARB before infection with wild-type EBOV. ARB caused significant dose-dependent inhibition of EBOV at all tested doses (*P* 0.0001; EC_{50} 2.7 μM) (Fig. 2A), with a selectivity index (SI) of 9 (Table 1). At the highest dose of 18.8 μM ARB, more than a 4-log inhibition of EBOV was observed. ARB appeared to protect, in a dose-dependent manner, HepG2 cells from EBOV-induced cytopathic effects (Fig. 2B). Specifically, increasing doses of ARB re-duced the number of rounded cells and increased the overall cell density in EBOV-infected cultures.

We have shown that ARB blocks HCV internalization into cells by slowing clathrin-mediated endocytosis and inhibiting fusion of HCV membranes with cellular membranes (18–21). Since EBOV also enters cells via an endocytotic process (22), we performed time-of-addition experiments. ARB was added to cells 24 h before, at the same time as, 1 h after, or 24 h after virus adsorption. ARB caused dose-dependent inhibition of EBOV when the compound was added to cells 24 h before or at the same time as (EC_{50} 4.9 μM) or 1 h after (EC_{50} 4.9 μM) virus infection (Fig. 3A). Compared to control treated cells, ARB caused significant suppression of EBOV infection at all tested doses when added before, during, or immediately after infection (*P* 0.03). In contrast, when ARB was added at 24 h postinfection, low doses of ARB (i.e., 2.35 and 4.7 μM) failed to inhibit EBOV. However, higher doses (i.e., 9.4 and 18.8 μM) of ARB still showed significant suppression (0.26-and 0.53-fold log suppression, respectively; *P* 0.002), although the level of suppression was far lower than when ARB was added before or during infection. These data suggest that ARB optimally inhibits EBOV infection when added before or during the early stages of infection and that ARB has some efficacy against established infection.

To further explore whether ARB targets an early stage in the EBOV life cycle, we used recombinant VSV expressing the EBOV glycoprotein (GP) from the Zaire isolate. ARB inhibited virus rep-lication when the drug was added to cells 1 h before, at the same time as, and 1 h after infection (Fig. 3B). Note, however, that maximal suppression of infection occurred when ARB was added prior to virus infection, and the efficacy of ARB declined as treat-ment was delayed. ARB did not inhibit replication of wild-type.

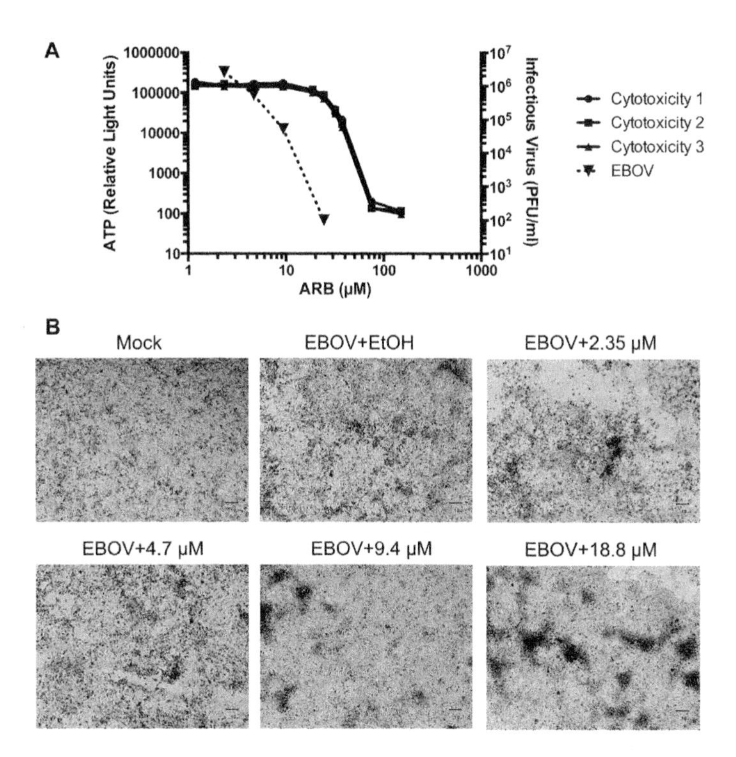

FIG 2 ARB inhibits EBOV. (A) Cytotoxicity and anti-EBOV profile of ARB on HepG2 cells. Left *y* axis, triplicate cultures of HepG2 cells were incubated with 0, 1.18, 2.35, 4.7, 9.4, 18.8, 24.4, 32, 37.6, 75.2, and 150.4 μM ARB prior to measurement of cellular ATP levels 3 days later. The experiment was performed three independent times, and the replicates are designated cytotoxicity 1, cytotoxicity 2, and cytotoxicity 3. Right *y* axis, ARB was incubated, in quadruplicate, with HepG2 cells for 24 h prior to infection with EBOV. Virus was adsorbed for 1 h (in the presence of ARB), followed by four cell washings with PBS and addition of medium with 0, 2.35, 4.7, 9.4, and 18.8 μM ARB. At 96 h postinfection, culture supernatants were harvested and diluted in fresh medium, and titers were determined on Vero E6 cells. Error bars are mostly contained within the symbols and represent standard error of the mean. (B) Light micrographs of the mock- and EBOV-infected cells, as well as cells infected with EBOV and treated with the indicated doses of ARB. Images were captured at 120 h postinfection.

VSV in this system, suggesting that the effect of ARB was directed against virus entry mediated by the EBOV GP. Collectively, these data suggest that ARB targets an early stage of the EBOV life cycle, most likely the entry step.

ARB inhibits other globally prevalent viruses. ARB was tested by NIAID's *in vitro* antiviral testing program. Table 1 shows that poliovirus, HHV-8, Tacaribe virus, and HBV were inhibited by ARB, with selectivity indexes (SIs) of 7.7, 6.2, 11, and 37, re-spectively. The primary hits against poliovirus, HHV-8, Tacaribe, and HBV were confirmed in secondary testing by NIAID. Finally, ARB inhibited HHV-8 replication to a similar degree as cidofovir (CDV), with the only difference being slightly increased cytotox-icity of ARB relative to CDV at the highest dose (60 μM) (Fig. 4).

TABLE 1 ARB inhibits multiple viruses[a]

Virus	Family	EC_{50} (μM)	CC_{50} (μM)	SI_{50} (μM)
Ebola virus				
Zaire	*Filoviridae*	2.7	24.4	9
Poliovirus		4.1	28.6	
type 3	*Picornaviridae*	3.2	9.6	7.7
HHV-8	*Herpesviridae*	1.6	60	37
Tacaribe		5.8	31.0	
virus	*Arenaviridae*	3.0	3.9	6.2
HBV	*Hepadnaviridae*	17.9	188	11

[a] EC_{50}, effective concentration of ARB that leads to 50% suppression of virus infection; CC_{50}, concentration of ARB that causes 50% cytotoxicity; SI_{50}, selectivity index, which is the ratio of CC_{50} to EC_{50}. Errors are standard deviations.

DISCUSSION

We show here that ARB inhibits multiple viruses of global medical significance, including EBOV. In support of our findings, suppression of EBOV by ARB was recently described, in supplemental data, in a large drug screen (23).

Mechanistically, we have previously shown that ARB inhibits HCV entry by blocking viral fusion (20, 21, 24) and that ARB also impairs clathrin-mediated endocytosis (18). Since the viruses in-hibited by ARB in this study may use clathrin to gain entry into cells (25–31), a possible unifying mode of action might be via

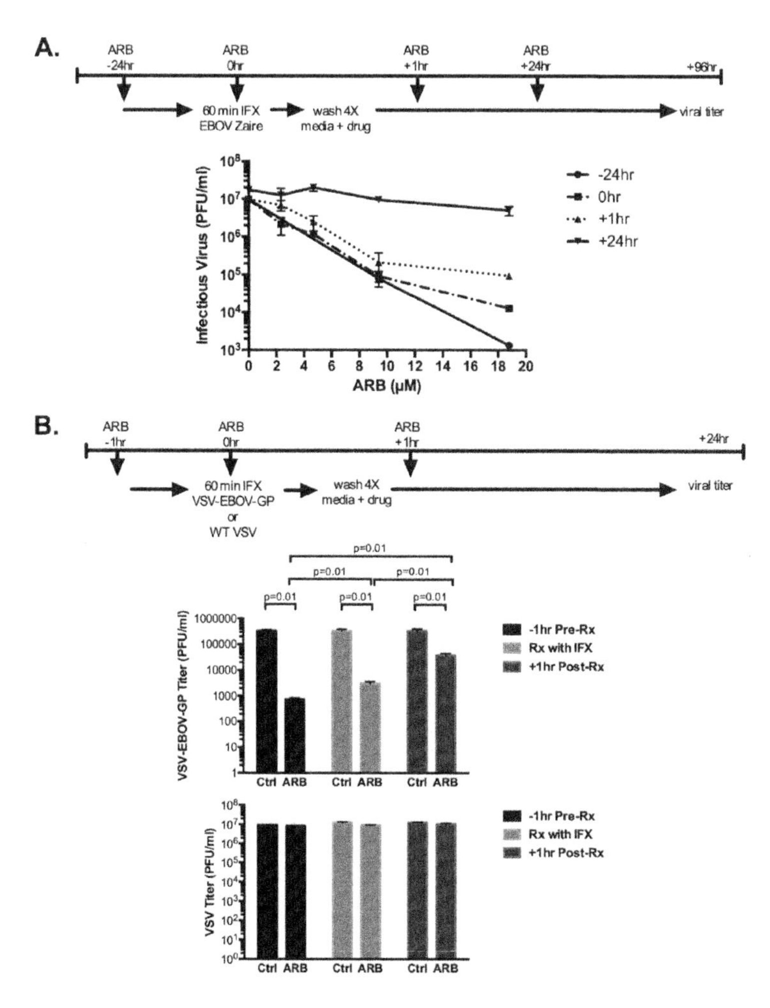

FIG 3 ARB inhibits an early stage of the EBOV life cycle. (A) HepG2 cells were treated with 0, 2.35, 4.7, 9.4, and 18.8 μM ARB for 24 h before infection (24 h), at the same time as infection (0

h), 1 h after infection (1 h), or 24 h after infection (24 h). Cells were infected with EBOV Zaire at an MOI of 0.5 for 1h and washed, and fresh medium containing ARB was added back to cultures. Infectious virus in culture supernatants harvested at 96h postinfection was determined by viral plaque assay on Vero E6 cells. Error bars represent the standard error of the mean for triplicate cultures. (B) Vero cells were pretreated for 1 h before infection (1 h) or at the same time as infection (0 h) with VSV pseudoviruses expressing EBOV Zaire glycoprotein or wild-type (WT) VSV. After an infection of 1h, cells were washed 4 times to remove unbound virus, and medium with vehicle or 10 μM ARB was added back to cells. ARB was also added to cells 1h after infection (1 h). Supernatants were harvested at 24h postinfection, and titers were determined on naive Vero cells. Values represent mean viral titers, and error bars represent the standard error of the mean for triplicate cultures.

blockade of virus entry. Time-of-addition experiments support this mode of action of ARB against EBOV. However, since EBOV and HHV-8 also enter cells by macropinocytosis (32–36), it will be important to discriminate actions of ARB on clathrin versus the macropinocytic routes of entry. In this regard, the other herpes-viruses not inhibited by ARB, including herpes simplex virus 1 (HSV-1) (37), HSV-2 and human cytomegalovirus (HCMV) (38), and Epstein-Barr virus (EBV) (39), all use clathrin-independent pathways to gain entry into cells. Finally, the possible membrane-associating actions of ARB (20, 21) need to be considered as poten-tial mechanisms for suppression of virus replication. In fact, since ARB is an indole-based hydrophobic molecule (Fig. 1), it displays a capacity for dual binding to both lipid membrane interfaces and ar-omatic protein residues (21). The physico-chemical properties of ARB may enable it to form supramolecular conformations through aromatic stacking interactions with selective amino acid residues of proteins (phenylalanine, tyrosine, and tryptophan). As such, ARB may impair many steps in the life cycle of viruses, including virus binding to cells, fusion of viral and cellular membranes during virus entry (20, 21, 24, 40–42), clathrin-mediated endocytosis (18), virus replication on intracellular membranes such as membranous webs (19, 43), and virus assembly and egress from cells.

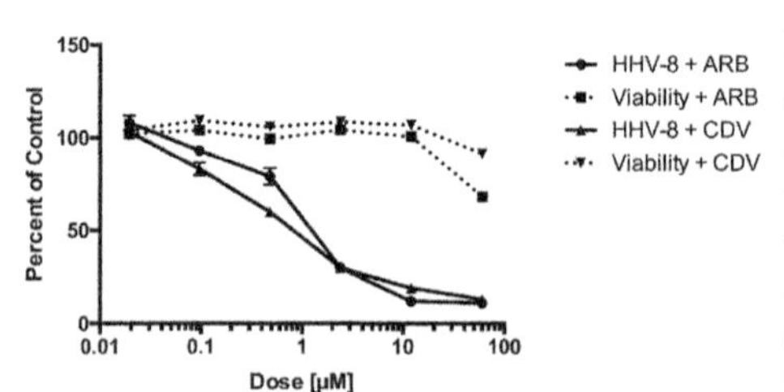

FIG 4 ARB inhibits HHV-8 replication to a similar extent as cidofovir. Hu-man BCBL-1 cells, which are infected with HHV-8 (50), were treated with ARB or CDV, HHV-8 DNA was quantified by reverse transcription-PCR (RT-PCR), and cell viability was measured by Cell Titer Glow assay (Promega) 7 days later. Error bars represent the standard error of the mean for triplicate cultures.

Why did ARB display clear antiviral activity against HHV-8 yet not inhibit other herpesviruses? Contrary to our findings, HSV-1 infection was previously shown to be inhibited by ARB and deriv-atives of the molecule (44). That study used human keratinocytes and a very low MOI (0.0001), which might account for the discor-dance with our study, which used a higher MOI (0.01). As de-scribed above, since HSV-1 uses clathrin-independent pathways, it may not be accessible to ARB's antiviral mode of action. It is also possible that the assay system might influence results. The HHV-8 assay derives from induction of lytic replication from latently in-fected BCBL-1 cells, while the HSV-1 assay deploys live virus in an acute-infection setting. Further studies are required to sort out these possibilities.

We confirmed a prior study showing that ARB inhibits *in vitro* replication of HBV (45). We further tested ARB in homozygous transgenic HBV mice (46). ARB was prepared and given to mice by daily oral gavage of 50 or 100 mg/kg/day of ARB for 14 days. Unfortunately, ARB did not inhibit HBV replication in this mouse model (data not shown). Pharmacokinetic studies were not per-formed due to budget limitations, so additional studies are required before unequivocal conclusions can be made.

ARB suppresses virus infection in the low micromolar range, which is higher than the value for directly acting antiviral (DAA) agents that target viral proteins or enzymes. We suspect that this is likely because ARB is a cell-targeting antiviral, based on multiple studies suggesting that ARB blocks virus entry by incorporating into cellular membranes and modifying their physico-chemical properties (reviewed in reference 12). Moreover, host-targeting compounds often function in higher concentration ranges than DAA compounds (47, 48). Finally, derivatives of ARB with improved bioactivity have been synthesized (44, 45), suggesting that it may be possible to lower the dose of ARB and improve the selectivity index.

ARB inhibited members of both *Filoviridae* and *Arenaviridae*, which are known to cause lethal hemorrhagic fevers in humans. It is noteworthy that ARB has been used clinically for decades in other countries, with minimal side effects and a good pharmacokinetic profile (9, 12, 49). Given that ARB seems to be most efficacious when administered prior to or at the same time as virus infection, ARB might be considered for prophylactic use in hemorrhagic fever outbreaks, which could limit the deadly spread of filoviruses and arenaviruses. Prophylactic use of ARB might also limit the risk of infection for health care workers when they treat infected subjects during outbreaks, and following repatriation of infected subjects. As a therapeutic antiviral drug, ARB could potentially act as a roadblock against spread of the virus to uninfected target cells. Additional studies at different multiplicities of infection may reveal the therapeutic potential of ARB for treatment of acute EBOV infection.

ACKNOWLEDGMENTS

We thank Gary Rohrabaugh of Good Earth Medicine LLC for providing arbidol. We also thank Michele Scian for NMR and mass spectrometry analysis of ARB. We thank Jessica Wagoner for technical support. The University of Washington utilized the nonclinical and preclinical services program offered by the National Institute of Allergy and Infectious Dis-eases.

The work was partly supported by NIH contract numbers HHSN272201100019I/HHSN27200001/B01, HHSN272201100016I, and HHSN272201000039I/HHSN27200001/A19. E.-I.P. was sup-ported by ANRS (French National Agency for Research on AIDS and Viral Hepatitis).

FUNDING INFORMATION

HHS | National Institutes of Health (NIH) provided funding to John D. Morrey and Donald F. Smee under contract number HHSN272201100019I. HHS | National Institutes of Health (NIH) provided funding to Donald F. Smee under contract number HHSN27200001/B01. HHS | National Insti-tutes of Health (NIH) provided funding to Donald F. Smee under contract number HHSN272201100016I. HHS | National Institutes of Health (NIH) provided funding to Mark N. Prichard under contract number HHSN272201000039Iz. HHS | National Institutes of Health (NIH) provided funding to John D. Morrey under contract number HHSN27200001/A19. This work was funded by the Agence Nationale de la Recherche (ANR).

REFERENCES

1. **Sulkowski MS, Jacobson IM, Nelson DR.** 2014. Daclatasvir plus sofos-buvir for HCV infection. N Engl J Med **370:**1560 –1561. http://dx.doi.org /10.1056/NEJMc1401726.
2. **Anonymous.** 1978. Ebola haemorrhagic fever in Sudan, 1976. Report of a WHO/International Study Team. Bull World Health Organ **56:**247–270.
3. **Shaffer JG, Grant DS, Schieffelin JS, Boisen ML, Goba A, Hartnett JN, Levy DC, Yenni RE, Moses LM, Fullah M, Momoh M, Fonnie M, Fonnie R, Kanneh L, Koroma VJ, Kargbo K, Ottomassathien D, Muncy IJ, Jones AB, Illick MM, Kulakosky PC, Haislip AM, Bishop CM, Elliot DH, Brown BL, Zhu H, Hastie KM, Andersen KG, Gire SK, Tabrizi S, Tariyal R, Stremlau M, Matschiner A, Sampey DB, Spence JS, Cross RW, Geisbert JB, Folarin OA, Happi CT, Pitts KR, Geske FJ, Geisbert TW, Saphire EO, Robinson JE, Wilson RB, Sabeti PC, Henderson LA, Khan SH, Bausch DG, Branco LM, et al.** 2014. Lassa fever in post-conflict Sierra Leone. PLoS Negl Trop Dis **8:**e2748. http://dx.doi.org/10.1371/journal.pntd.0002748.
4. **Sayler KA, Barbet AF, Chamberlain C, Clapp WL, Alleman R, Loeb JC, Lednicky JA.** 2014. Isolation of Tacaribe virus, a Caribbean arenavirus, from host-seeking Amblyomma americanum ticks in Florida. PLoS One **9:**e115769. http://dx.doi.org/10.1371/journal.pone.0115769.
5. **Moore PS, Chang Y.** 1995. Detection of herpesvirus-like DNA sequences in Kaposi's sarcoma in patients with and without HIV infection. N Engl J Med **332:**1181–1185. http://dx.doi.org/10.1056/NEJM199505043321801.
6. **Sutter RW, Platt L, Mach O, Jafari H, Aylward RB.** 2014. The new polio eradication end game: rationale and supporting evidence. J Infect Dis **210**(Suppl 1)**:**S434 –S438. http://dx.doi.org/10.1093/infdis/jiu222.
7. **Lozano R, Naghavi M, Foreman K, Lim S, Shibuya K, Aboyans V, Abraham J, Adair T, Aggarwal R, Ahn SY, Alvarado M, Anderson HR, Anderson LM, Andrews KG, Atkinson C, Baddour LM, Barker-Collo S, Bartels DH, Bell ML, Benjamin EJ, Bennett D, Bhalla K, Bikbov B, Bin Abdulhak A, Birbeck G, Blyth F, Bolliger I, Boufous S, Bucello C, Burch M, Burney P, Carapetis J, Chen H, Chou D, Chugh SS, Coffeng LE, Colan SD, Colquhoun S, Colson KE, Condon J, Connor MD, Cooper LT, Corriere M, Cortinovis M, de Vaccaro KC, Couser W, Cowie BC, Criqui MH, Cross M, Dabhadkar KC, et al.** 2012. Global and regional mortality from 235 causes of death for 20 age groups in 1990 and 2010: a systematic analysis for the Global Burden of Disease Study 2010. Lancet **380:**2095–2128. http://dx.doi.org/10.1016/S0140-6736(12)61728-0.
8. **Gagarinova VM, Ignat'eva GS, Sinitskaia LV, Ivanova AM, Rodina MA, Tur'eva AV.** 1993. The new chemical preparation arbidol: its prophylactic efficacy during influenza epidemics. Zh Mikrobiol Epidemiol Immuno-biol **1993:**40 – 43.
9. **Boriskin YS, Leneva IA, Pécheur EI, Polyak SJ.** 2008. Arbidol: a broad-spectrum antiviral

compound that blocks viral fusion. Curr Med Chem **15:**997–1005. http://dx.doi.org/10.2174/092986708784049658.

10. **Brooks MJ, Burtseva EI, Ellery PJ, Marsh GA, Lew AM, Slepushkin AN, Crowe SM, Tannock GA.** 2012. Antiviral activity of arbidol, a broad-spectrum drug for use against respiratory viruses, varies according to test conditions. J Med Virol **84:**170 –181. http://dx.doi.org/10.1002/jmv.22234.
11. **Zhao C, Zhao Y, Chai H, Gong P.** 2006. Synthesis and in vitro anti-hepatitis B virus activities of some ethyl 5-hydroxy-1H-indole-3-carboxylates. Bioorg Med Chem **14:**2552–2558. http://dx.doi.org/10.1016 /j.bmc.2005.11.033.
12. **Blaising J, Polyak SJ, Pécheur EI.** 2014. Arbidol as a broad-spectrum antiviral: an update. Antiviral Res **107:**84 –94. http://dx.doi.org/10.1016/j.antiviral.2014.04.006.
13. **Prichard MN, Williams JD, Komazin-Meredith G, Khan AR, Price NB, Jefferson GM, Harden EA, Hartline CB, Peet NP, Bowlin TL.** 2013. Synthesis and antiviral activities of methylenecyclopropane analogs with 6-alkoxy and 6-alkylthio substitutions that exhibit broad-spectrum anti-viral activity against human herpesviruses. Antimicrob Agents Chemother **57:**3518 –3527. http://dx.doi.org/10.1128/AAC.00429-13.
14. **Sells MA, Chen ML, Acs G.** 1987. Production of hepatitis B virus particles in Hep G2 cells transfected with cloned hepatitis B virus DNA. Proc Natl Acad Sci U S A **84:**1005–1009. http://dx.doi.org/10.1073/pnas.84.4.1005.
15. **Iyer RP, Jin Y, Roland A, Morrey JD, Mounir S, Korba B.** 2004. Phosphorothioate di- and trinucleotides as a novel class of anti-hepatitis B virus agents. Antimicrob Agents Chemother **48:**2199 –2205. http://dx.doi.org/10.1128/AAC.48.6.2199-2205.2004.
16. **Barnard DL, Hubbard VD, Smee DF, Sidwell RW, Watson KG, Tucker SP, Reece PA.** 2004. In vitro activity of expanded-spectrum pyridazinyl oxime ethers related to pirodavir: novel capsid-binding inhibitors with potent antipicornavirus activity. Antimicrob Agents Chemother **48:**1766 – 1772. http://dx.doi.org/10.1128/AAC.48.5.1766-1772.2004.
17. **Gowen BB, Wong MH, Jung KH, Sanders AB, Mendenhall M, Bailey KW, Furuta Y, Sidwell RW.** 2007. In vitro and in vivo activities of T-705 against arenavirus and bunyavirus infections. Antimicrob Agents Che-mother **51:**3168 –3176. http://dx.doi.org/10.1128/AAC.00356-07.
18. **Blaising J, Levy PL, Polyak SJ, Stanifer M, Boulant S, Pécheur EI.** 2013. Arbidol inhibits viral entry by interfering with clathrin-dependent traf-ficking. Antiviral Res **100:**215–219. http://dx.doi.org/10.1016/j.antiviral.2013.08.008.
19. **Boriskin YS, Pecheur EI, Polyak SJ.** 2006. Arbidol: a broad-spectrum antiviral that inhibits acute and chronic HCV infection. Virol J **3:**56. http: //dx.doi.org/10.1186/1743-422X-3-56.
20. **Pécheur EI, Lavillette D, Alcaras F, Molle J, Boriskin YS, Roberts M, Cosset FL, Polyak SJ.** 2007. Biochemical mechanism of hepatitis C virus inhibition by the broad-spectrum antiviral arbidol. Biochemistry **46:** 6050 – 6059. http://dx.doi.org/10.1021/bi700181j.
21. **Teissier E, Zandomeneghi G, Loquet A, Lavillette D, Lavergne JP, Montserret R, Cosset FL, Bockmann A, Meier BH, Penin F, Pécheur EI.** 2011. Mechanism of inhibition of enveloped virus membrane fusion by the antiviral drug arbidol. PLoS One **6:**e15874. http://dx.doi.org/10.1371 /journal.pone.0015874.
22. **Jae LT, Brummelkamp TR.** 2015. Emerging intracellular receptors for hemorrhagic fever viruses. Trends Microbiol **23:**392– 400. http://dx.doi.org/10.1016/j.tim.2015.04.006.

23. **Johansen LM, DeWald LE, Shoemaker CJ, Hoffstrom BG, Lear-Rooney CM, Stossel A, Nelson E, Delos SE, Simmons JA, Grenier JM, Pierce LT, Pajouhesh H, Lehár J, Hensley LE, Glass PJ, White JM, Olinger GG.**
2015. A screen of approved drugs and molecular probes identifies thera-peutics with anti-Ebola virus activity. Sci Transl Med **7:**290ra289.

24. **Haid S, Pietschmann T, Pécheur EI.** 2009. Low pH-dependent hepatitis C virus membrane fusion depends on E2 integrity, target lipid composi-tion, and density of virus particles. J Biol Chem **284:**17657–17667. http: //dx.doi.org/10.1074/jbc.M109.014647.

25. **Cooper A, Shaul Y.** 2006. Clathrin-mediated endocytosis and lysosomal cleavage of hepatitis B virus capsid-like core particles. J Biol Chem **281:** 16563–16569. http://dx.doi.org/10.1074/jbc.M601418200.

26. **Helle F, Dubuisson J.** 2008. Hepatitis C virus entry into host cells. Cell Mol Life Sci **65:**100 –112. http://dx.doi.org/10.1007/s00018-007-7291-8.

27. **Willingmann P, Barnert H, Zeichhardt H, Habermehl KO.** 1989. Re-covery of structurally intact and infectious poliovirus type 1 from HeLa cells during receptor-mediated endocytosis. Virology **168:**417– 420. http: //dx.doi.org/10.1016/0042-6822(89)90286-9.

28. **Akula SM, Naranatt PP, Walia NS, Wang FZ, Fegley B, Chandran B.**
2003. Kaposi's sarcoma-associated herpesvirus (human herpesvirus 8) in-fection of human fibroblast cells occurs through endocytosis. J Virol **77:** 7978 –7990. http://dx.doi.org/10.1128/JVI.77.14.7978-7990.2003.

29. **Lakadamyali M, Rust MJ, Zhuang X.** 2006. Ligands for clathrin-mediated endocytosis are differentially sorted into distinct populations of early endosomes. Cell **124:**997–1009. http://dx.doi.org/10.1016/j.cell.2005.12.038.

30. **Inoue Y, Tanaka N, Tanaka Y, Inoue S, Morita K, Zhuang M, Hattori T, Sugamura K.** 2007. Clathrin-dependent entry of severe acute respira-tory syndrome coronavirus into target cells expressing ACE2 with the cytoplasmic tail deleted. J Virol **81:**8722– 8729. http://dx.doi.org/10.1128 /JVI.00253-07.

31. **Vela EM, Zhang L, Colpitts TM, Davey RA, Aronson JF.** 2007. Arena-virus entry occurs through a cholesterol-dependent, non-caveolar, clath-rin-mediated endocytic mechanism. Virology **369:**1–11. http://dx.doi.org /10.1016/j.virol.2007.07.014.

32. **Saeed MF, Kolokoltsov AA, Albrecht T, Davey RA.** 2010. Cellular entry of Ebola virus involves uptake by a macropinocytosis-like mechanism and subsequent trafficking through early and late endosomes. PLoS Pathog **6:**e1001110. http://dx.doi.org/10.1371/journal.ppat.1001110.

33. **Nanbo A, Imai M, Watanabe S, Noda T, Takahashi K, Neumann G, Halfmann P, Kawaoka Y.** 2010. Ebolavirus is internalized into host cells via macropinocytosis in a viral glycoprotein-dependent manner. PLoS Pathog **6:**e1001121. http://dx.doi.org/10.1371/journal.ppat.1001121.

34. **Aleksandrowicz P, Marzi A, Biedenkopf N, Beimforde N, Becker S, Hoenen T, Feldmann H, Schnittler HJ.** 2011. Ebola virus enters host cells by macropinocytosis and clathrin-mediated endocytosis. J Infect Dis **204**(Suppl 3)**:**S957–S967. http://dx.doi.org/10.1093/infdis/jir326.

35. **Raghu H, Sharma-Walia N, Veettil MV, Sadagopan S, Chandran B.** 2009. Kaposi's sarcoma-associated herpesvirus utilizes an actin polymer-ization-dependent macropinocytic pathway to enter human dermal mi-crovascular endothelial and human umbilical vein endothelial cells. J Vi-rol **83:**4895– 4911. http://dx.doi.org/10.1128/JVI.02498-08.

36. **Greene W, Gao SJ.** 2009. Actin dynamics regulate multiple endosomal steps during Kaposi's sarcoma-associated herpesvirus entry and traffick-ing in endothelial cells. PLoS Pathog **5:**e1000512. http://dx.doi.org/10.1371/journal.ppat.1000512.

37. **Akhtar J, Shukla D.** 2009. Viral entry mechanisms: cellular and viral mediators of herpes simplex virus entry. FEBS J **276:**7228 –7236. http://dx.doi.org/10.1111/j.1742-4658.2009.07402.x.

38. **Vanarsdall AL, Wisner TW, Lei H, Kazlauskas A, Johnson DC.** 2012. PDGF receptor-alpha does not promote HCMV entry into epithelial and endothelial cells but increased quantities stimulate entry by an abnormal pathway. PLoS Pathog **8:**e1002905. http://dx.doi.org/10.1371/journal.ppat.1002905.

39. **Nemerow GR, Cooper NR.** 1984. Early events in the infection of human B lymphocytes by Epstein-Barr virus: the internalization process. Virology **132:**186 –198. http://dx.doi.org/10.1016/0042-6822(84)90102-8.

40. **Teissier E, Penin F, Pécheur EI.** 2011. Targeting cell entry of enveloped viruses as an antiviral strategy. Molecules **16:**221–250. http://dx.doi.org /10.3390/molecules16010221.

41. **Nasser ZH, Swaminathan K, Muller P, Downard KM.** 2013. Inhibition of influenza hemagglutinin with the antiviral inhibitor arbidol using a proteomics based approach and mass spectrometry. Antiviral Res **100:** 399 – 406. http://dx.doi.org/10.1016/j.antiviral.2013.08.021.

42. **Delogu I, Pastorino B, Baronti C, Nougairede A, Bonnet E, de Lam-ballerie X.** 2011. In vitro antiviral activity of arbidol against Chikungunya virus and characteristics of a selected resistant mutant. Antiviral Res **90:** 99 –107. http://dx.doi.org/10.1016/j.antiviral.2011.03.182.

43. **Moradpour D, Penin F, Rice CM.** 2007. Replication of hepatitis C virus. Nat Rev Microbiol **5:**453– 463. http://dx.doi.org/10.1038/nrmicro1645.

44. **Perfetto B, Filosa R, De Gregorio V, Peduto A, La Gatta A, de Caprariis P, Tufano MA, Donnarumma G.** 2014. In vitro antiviral and immuno-modulatory activity of arbidol and structurally related derivatives in her-pes simplex virus type 1-infected human keratinocytes (HaCat). J Med Microbiol **63:**1474 –1483. http://dx.doi.org/10.1099/jmm.0.076612-0.

45. **Chai H, Zhao Y, Zhao C, Gong P.** 2006. Synthesis and in vitro anti-hepatitis B virus activities of some ethyl 6-bromo-5-hydroxy-1H-indole-3-carboxylates. Bioorg Med Chem **14:**911–917. http://dx.doi.org/10.1016 /j.bmc.2005.08.041.

46. **Guidotti LG, Matzke B, Schaller H, Chisari FV.** 1995. High-level hepa-titis B virus replication in transgenic mice. J Virol **69:**6158 – 6169.

47. **Sainz B, Jr, Barretto N, Martin DN, Hiraga N, Imamura M, Hussain S, Marsh KA, Yu X, Chayama K, Alrefai WA, Uprichard SL.** 2012. Iden-tification of the Niemann-Pick C1-like 1 cholesterol absorption receptor as a new hepatitis C virus entry factor. Nat Med **18:**281–285. http://dx.doi.org/10.1038/nm.2581.

48. **Lupberger J, Zeisel MB, Xiao F, Thumann C, Fofana I, Zona L, Davis C, Mee CJ, Turek M, Gorke S, Royer C, Fischer B, Zahid MN, Lavillette D, Fresquet J, Cosset FL, Rothenberg SM, Pietschmann T, Patel AH, Pessaux P, Doffoel M, Raffelsberger W, Poch O, McKeating JA, Brino L, Baumert TF.** 2011. EGFR and EphA2 are host factors for hepatitis C virus entry and possible targets for antiviral therapy. Nat Med **17:**589 –595. http://dx.doi.org/10.1038/nm.2341.

49. **Brooks MJ, Sasadeusz JJ, Tannock GA.** 2004. Antiviral chemotherapeu-tic agents against respiratory viruses: where are we now and what's in the pipeline? Curr Opin Pulm Med **10:**197–

203. http://dx.doi.org/10.1097 /00063198-200405000-00009.

50. **Renne R, Zhong W, Herndier B, McGrath M, Abbey N, Kedes D, Ganem D.** 1996. Lytic growth of Kaposi's sarcoma-associated herpesvirus (human herpesvirus 8) in culture. Nat Med **2:**342–346. http://dx.doi.org /10.1038/nm0396-342.

Arbidol inhibits viral entry by interfering with clathrin-dependent trafficking

Julie Blaising [a,1,2], Pierre L. Lévy [b,1], Stephen J. Polyak [c], Megan Stanifer [d], Steeve Boulant [d,⇑,1], Eve-Isabelle Pécheur [a,⇑,1,2]

[a] IBCP, UMR 5086, CNRS, University of Lyon, Lyon, France

[b] CRCL, Inserm U1052, CNRS 5286, University of Lyon, Lyon, France

[c] Dept of Laboratory Medicine and Global Health, University of Washington, Seattle, WA, USA

[d] Dept of Infectious Diseases, Virology, CHS Nachwuchsgruppe am CellNetworks Cluster und DKFZ, University of Heidelberg, Germany

Abstract

Arbidol (ARB) is a broad-spectrum antiviral displaying activity against a number of enveloped and non-enveloped viruses. It was described as a viral entry inhibitor and shown to interact at the molecular level with lipid membranes and viral fusion glycoproteins to impede viral entry and fusion. However its mechanism of action at the cellular level remains unknown. Here, by using live-cell confocal imaging and the hepatitis C virus as a model virus, we show that ARB affects clathrin-mediated endocytosis by impeding dynamin-2-induced membrane scission. Moreover it induces the intracellular accumulation of clathrin-coated structures where viral particles are trapped. Collectively, our results shed light on the mechanistic aspects of ARB antiviral activity and suggest that ARB could prevent cell infection by viruses that enter through clathrin-mediated endocytosis.

Antiviral drug development has led to significant advances in the control of globally prevalent viral infections including hepatitis C virus (HCV) and human immunodeficiency virus (HIV). Nonetheless, there are current gaps in the armamentarium against (re-)emerging viruses causing problems for global control and eradication, especially in cases of major outbreaks. Arbidol (ARB), a drug already licensed in Russia and China against flu, was de-scribed as a broad-spectrum antiviral able to prevent infection of enveloped and non-enveloped viruses (Boriskin et al., 2008; Brooks et al., 2004, 2012; Delogu et al., 2011). It was shown to inhibit viral replication

⇑ Corresponding authors. Address: CHS Nachwuchsgruppe am CellNetworks Cluster und DKFZ, Department of Infectious Diseases, Virology, Im Neuenheimer Feld 581, University Heidelberg, Germany. Tel.: +49 6221 42 1560 (S. Boulant), CRCL, Inserm U1052, CNRS 5286, University of Lyon, 69424 Lyon cedex 03, France. Tel.: +33 4 7268 1975 (E.-I. Pécheur).

E-mail addresses: s.boulant@dkfz-heidelberg.de (S. Boulant), eve-isabelle.pe-cheur@inserm.fr (E.-I. Pécheur).

[1] These authors contributed equally to this work.

[2] Present address: CRCL, Inserm U1052, CNRS 5286, University of Lyon, Lyon, France.

(Boriskin et al., 2006; Brooks et al., 2012; Chai et al., 2006; Delogu et al., 2011) and entry (reviewed in Boriskin et al., 2008; Leneva et al., 2009; Teissier et al., 2010).
Cell entry of viruses is an attractive target to therapeutic intervention, with opportunities to protect 'naive' cells. At the atomic and molecular levels, ARB was shown to display a dual binding capacity: on lipid membrane interfaces (Pécheur et al., 2007; Teissier et al., 2011; Villalain, 2010) and on specific residues within the viral fusion glycopro-tein(s) (Leneva et al., 2009; Teissier et al., 2011), thereby altering membrane fluidity, hindering conformational rearrangements in viral glycoproteins and blocking viral fusion. In spite of these documented studies, the mechanism by which ARB blocks viral entry at the cellular level remains unknown. Here we investigated this feature by using live-cell confocal imaging and HCV as a model of enveloped virus.

We first studied the effect of ARB on HCV intracellular traffick-ing in Huh7.5 hepatoma cells. Cells were pretreated or not with 11 μM ARB and synchronized on ice for 1 h with HCV grown in cell culture (HCVcc, MOI 1). This concentration was chosen since it did not cause any cytotoxicity, constituted the IC_{50} of HCV infectivity and induced maximal inhibition of HCV fusion in vitro (Blaising et al., 2013; Boriskin et al., 2006; Haid et al., 2009; Pécheur et al., 2007). After washing unbound virus, cells were transferred to 37 °C to initiate viral entry, then fixed at early (15 min) and late (60 min) stages of infection, and co-immunostained for HCV core and markers of early or late endocytic compartments (clathrin or Lamp1 respectively), as described (Blaising et al., 2013). In the ab-sence of ARB, HCV mainly colocalized with clathrin-positive struc-tures 15 min post-infection; after 60 min, particles no longer colocalized with clathrin but coincided with Lamp1 (Fig. 1A; quan-tification in B), indicating that the virus had moved from endocytic vesicles to late endosomes. Strikingly, in ARB-treated cells, virions were confined in clathrin-positive structures at early and late times post-infection (Fig. 1), suggesting that ARB impedes HCV intracellular trafficking from early to late endosomal compartments.

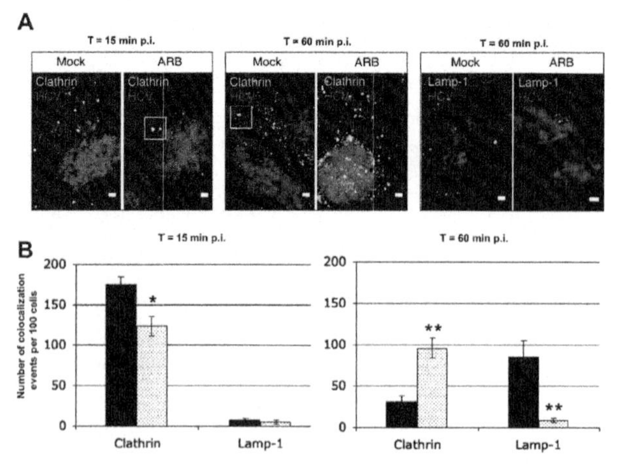

Fig. 1. ARB impedes HCV intracellular trafficking. (A) Huh7.5 cells were mock- or pre-treated with 11 μM ARB (99% pure, dissolved in ethanol/H_2O 10:90 v:v) for 30 min at 37°C, and incubated with HCVcc clone JFH-1 (prepared and titrated as in (Wakita et al., 2005); 9.9 10e5 ffu/ml; MOI 1) for 1 h at 4°C, in medium containing ARB or not. Unbound virus was washed off with cold PBS, culture medium with or without ARB was added and cells were shifted to 37°C to initiate viral cell entry. Coverslips were fixed with 2% PFA at early (15 min) and late (60 min) stages of infection, co-immunostained for HCV core (red) and clathrin light chain or Lamp-1 (endo-lysosomal marker) (green) and imaged using a Leica Confocal Spectral TCS SP5 AOBS. Bar, 2

μm. (B) Quantification of the number of colocalization events between HCVcc and indicated endosomal marker, counted in 100 cells, mock- or ARB-treated; 15 min/60 min, time after transfer of HCV-infected cells to 37°C. Results are mean ± SD from three independent experiments. Black bars, mock; shaded bars, ARB-treated cells. *, $p < 0.01$; **, $p < 0.005$ (unpaired Student's t test). (For interpretation of the references to colour in this figure legend, the reader is referred to the web version of this article.)

We then followed clathrin-mediated endocytosis (CME) into living cells by time-lapse confocal microscopy, using HCV-pseudo-typed retroviral particles (HCVpp, Bartosch et al., 2003; Blaising et al., 2013). Concentrated HCVpp were labeled with the lipophilic rhodamine dye R_{18}, thoroughly purified and characterized as described in (Blaising et al., 2013). Huh7.5 cells expressing a clathrin-GFP fusion protein, pretreated or not with ARB, were infected with R_{18}-HCVpp. After temperature shift, particle internalization was followed by imaging five times per second for several minutes (Movie S1). A typical HCV entry event is shown Fig. 2A (top): after binding, HCV associated with a discrete clathrin-GFP spot (30s). The clathrin-GFP signal around the virion then increased (60s), followed by a rapid disappearance of the clathrin signal (88s), suggesting the internalization of the virus via clathrin-coated pits (CCPs), followed by rapid uncoating of clathrin-coated vesicles (CCVs). In ARB-treated cells, HCV remained confined in CCVs for a greater period of time (305s). Tracking analyses revealed an overall impediment to HCV movement and speed in ARB- vs mock-treated cells (Fig. 2A bottom; 2B; Movie S2).

Quantification of the number of internalized R_{18}-HCVpp normalized to the cell area was performed as a function of time. In untreated cells, the number of HCV particles in cells increased over the first 15 min, corresponding to the virion internalization phase (Mock, Fig. 2C). It then decreased over the next 50 min, cor-responding to HCVpp fusion with endosome membranes, associated with disappearance of the fluorescence signal from viral particles or degradation of HCVpp. In the presence of ARB, the number of cell-associated virions was significantly lower than in mock-treated cells over the first 15 min (ARB, Fig. 2C; see Fig. 4D). This number drastically increased to reach a plateau at 45 min, and was stable even when longer kinetics were followed (not shown). This suggests the absence of fusion events and/or the confinement of HCV inside stabilized clathrin-coated struc-tures in ARB-treated cells. We next quantified the colocalization events over time of clathrin-coated structures with HCV (Fig. 2D). In mock-treated cells, the number of colocalization events was constant within the first 20 min. This corresponds to the clathrin-dependent uptake phase of HCV by cells. This number decreased at later times, when viruses have already entered cells. Upon ARB treatment, fewer virions were found associated with clathrin and this number did not significantly increase over time. This agrees with our data shown in Fig. 2A and suggests that ARB hinders HCV internalization via CCVs into hepatoma cells, leading to virion confinement in CCVs.

To test whether ARB could slow down CME as a general mechanism, we addressed both the impact of ARB on viruses known to infect cells in a clathrin-dependent manner and on the cellular uptake of clathrin-specific cargo. For this purpose we used BSC-1 cells, a canonical model system to study CME (Ehrlich et al., 2004; Blaising et al., 2013; Boulant et al., 2011). As observed with Huh7.5 cells, ARB displayed cytotoxicity only at high doses (Fig. S1). We first assessed ARB antiviral activity against vesicular stomatitis virus (VSV) and reovirus, which enter cells by CME (Cureton et al., 2009; Schulz et al., 2012). Pretreating BSC-1 cells with ARB prevented VSV infection in a dose-dependent manner, and

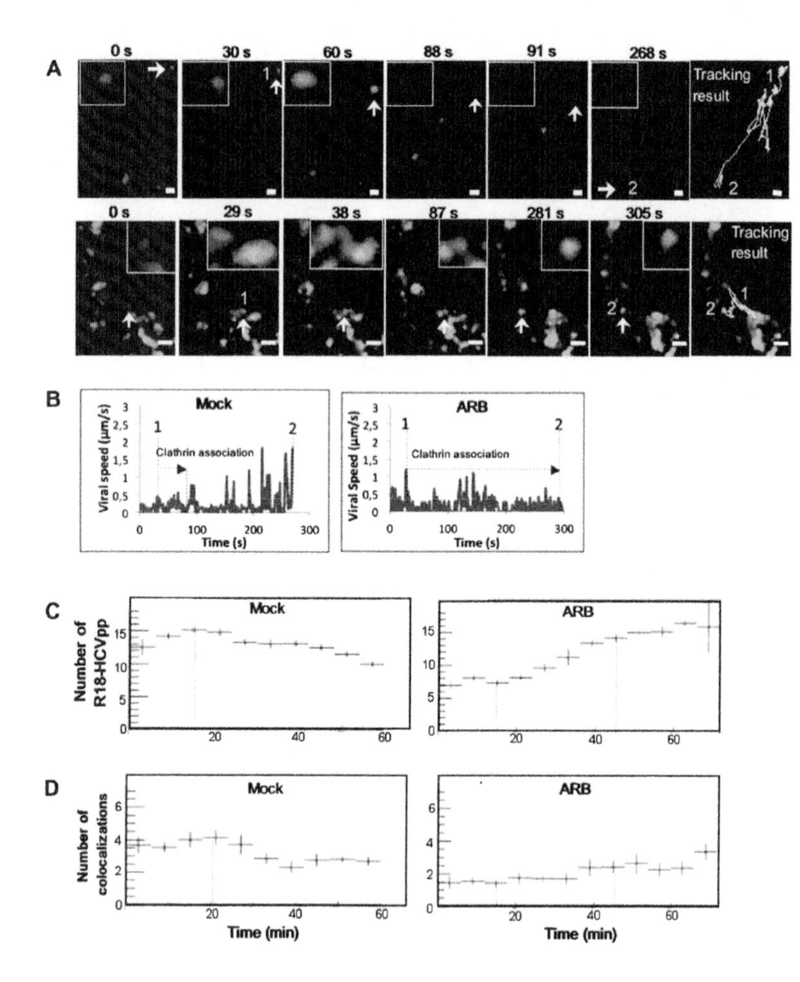

Fig. 2. ARB hinders HCV internalization. (A) Snapshots of R_{18}-labeled HCVpp (red), internalized in GFP-clathrin-coated pits (green) in mock-treated cells (Mock; Movie S1) or treated with 11 µM ARB (ARB; Movie S2). HCVpp trajectories were reconstituted using ImageJ plug-in Manual_Tracking (http://rsbweb.nih.gov/ij/plugins/track/track.html). Yellow trackings indicate beginning (1) and end (2) of HCVpp trajectory. Bar, 2 µm. (B) Viral speed recorded from similar analyses of trajectories as in A, in the absence (Mock) or presence of ARB; CME, clathrin-mediated endocytosis. (C) Number of R_{18}-HCVpp normalized to a cell area of 2000 µm^2, as a function of time in mock- or ARB-treated cells. To estimate the measurement error on the number of HCV particles, the mean value and standard deviation of these quantities were calculated using counts over a 6 min-period. Each symbol corresponds to counts performed on six individual cells. The ROOT TEfficiency method based on the Clopper–Pearson confidence limits was used (http://root.cern.ch/root/html/TEfficiency.html), since the number of events evaluated was not following a gaussian distribution. (D) Number of colocalization events between clathrin-coated structures and

HCV normalized to a cell area of 2000 μm^2, as a function of time in mock- or ARB-treated cells, performed similarly as in C. (For interpretation of the references to colour in this figure legend, the reader is referred to the web version of this article.)

IC_{50}s of ARB for VSV and HCV were similar (Fig. S2A) [14 and 11 μM, respectively], strongly suggestive of a similar inhibitory mechanism of HCV and VSV infection. ARB reduced by 80% the number of reovirus-infected cells (Fig. S2B), but did not alter infec-tion by infectious subvirion particles (ISVPs), which enter cells independently of CME (Maginnis et al., 2008; Martinez et al., 1996).

We next monitored the uptake of transferrin (Trf), a prototype cargo for CCV. In mock-treated BSC-1 cells, Trf was detected within endosomal compartments in the perinuclear region (Fig. 3A). In ARB-treated cells, very little Trf was detected intracellularly, except few Trf-loaded endosomes (Fig. 3B). Similar results were ob-tained using Huh7.5 cells (Fig. S3). This suggests that ARB affects CME, in line with ARB impediment on HCV particle uptake.

To gain further details on the mechanisms of ARB, we monitored the impact of ARB treatment on the dynamics of CCP formation using BSC-1 cells expressing adaptor protein-2 (AP2) fused to GFP, as described (Blaising et al., 2013; Boulant et al., 2011). Cells were mock- or ARB-treated, observed by live-cell confocal microscopy and CCP formation lifetime was determined as in (Boulant et al., 2011). In mock-treated cells, most pits were dynamic (appearing/disappearing) during the 300s-imaging period, as seen on kymographs (time projections, Fig. 4A), CCP lifetime distribution (Fig. 4C) and in movies S3, S4, S5. In ARB-treated cells, the number of CCPs forming at the cell surface decreased (Fig. 4B) and the number of long-lived structures increased (Fig. 4C), indicating that ARB alters CME dynamics by slowing down CCP formation at the cell surface (Movies S6, S7, S8).

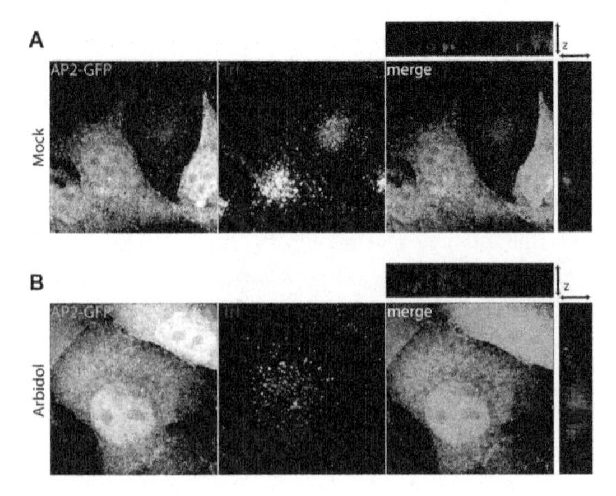

Fig. 3. ARB impairs clathrin-dependent endocytosis in BSC-1 cells. African green monkey kidney BSC-1 cells expressing AP2 σ2 subunit fused to eGFP were plated 16 h at 37°C prior to experiment. Cells were either mock- (A) or ARB-pretreated (B) at a final concentration of 11 μM in complete DMEM medium for 15 min. Cells were washed twice with PBS and human Trf (50 μg/ml) was added to the cells in serum-free medium, in the presence or absence (mock) of 11 μM ARB at 37°C. After a 7 min-uptake, cells were fixed with 4% PFA, mounted on slide with prolonged gold and observed by fluorescence confocal microscopy. (For interpretation of the references to colour in this figure legend, the reader is referred to the web version of this article.)

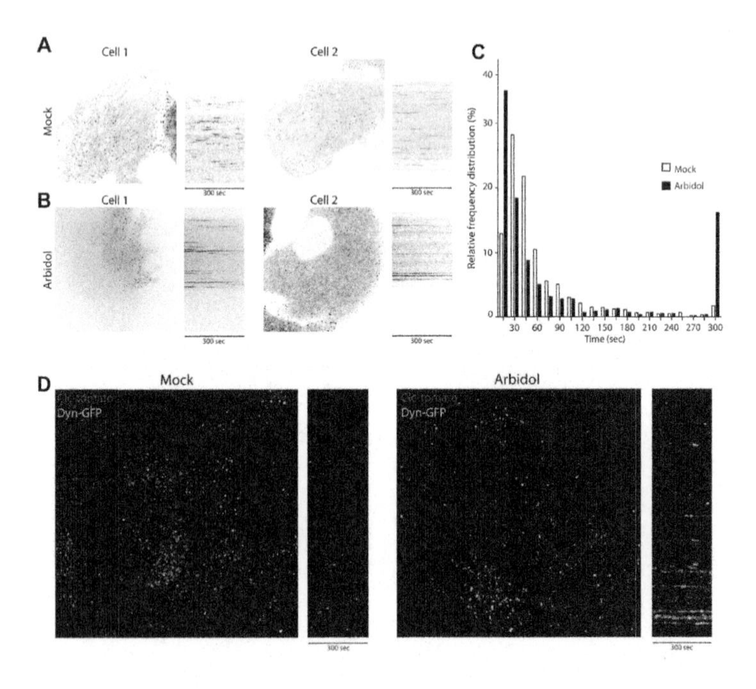

Fig. 4. ARB prevents pinching of CCPs from the plasma membrane. BSC-1 cells expressing AP2 (subunit σ2)-GFP were seeded 16 h prior to experiments in Labteck live cell chambers.
Cells were washed once with PBS and medium was replaced by imaging medium (DMEM 2% FCS, phenol red-free) containing (B) or not (mock) 11 μM ARB (A). Dynamics of coated pit formation was monitored by live-cell spinning disk confocal microscopy, imaging every 3 s for a total time of 300 s. Clathrin-coated structures were identified using a Mat-lab IMAB software (Boulant et al., 2011) and CCPs lifetimes were determined. C. The lifetime distribution of CCPs in mock-treated cells (from A; Movies S3–5) and ARB-treated cells (from B; Movies S6–8) was plotted using a bin of 15 s. D. BSC-1 cells expressing Clc-tomato and Dyn-GFP were seeded 16 h prior to experiments. Cells were processed and imaged as described above. (For interpretation of the references to colour in this figure legend, the reader is referred to the web version of this article.)

To pinpoint how ARB affects CME, we used BSC-1 cells co-expressing clathrin light chain fused to the fluorescent protein tomato (Clc-tomato) and dynamin-2 fused to GFP (Dyn-GFP). Dynamin-2 is a GTPase involved in the final step of CCV formation, recruited to membranes of fully-formed CCPs and promoting CCP pinching from the plasma membrane. In mock-treated cells, Dyn-GFP was recruited just prior to the disappearance of clathrin-coated structures (Fig. 4D left panels). Conversely, in ARB-treated cells, Dyn-GFP was recruited to coated structures but this was not associated with disappearance of the clathrin signal (Fig. 4D right panels). We sometimes observed multiple Dyn-GFP recruitments to the same frozen clathrin structures (not shown). ARB would therefore affect CME not by blocking dynamin-2 recruitment but by preventing dynamin-2-induced membrane scission.

In summary, our study provides for the first time molecular de-tails of ARB's mechanism of action on viral entry, with the following conclusions: (i) ARB hinders HCV endosomal trafficking: virions get trapped in clathrin-positive structures and cannot be properly delivered to endosomal compartments, thereby preventing infection; (ii) ARB globally impedes CME and induces the intracellular accumulation of clathrin-coated structures, and acts at the most early stage of membrane scission leading to CCP formation; (iii) this could constitute a general mechanism of action, since ARB also efficiently hinders cell infection by VSV and reovirus which enter cells by CME as well.

Since ARB displays tropism for lipid bilayers, as we showed previously (Pécheur et al., 2007; Teissier et al., 2011), we propose that ARB, by inserting into cellular membranes, would impregnate these membranes thereby impeding the release of CCV from the plasma membrane. This effect might be at the protein level, pre-venting the recruitment/activation of proteins which co-act with dynamin-2 to release the CCV or at the lipid level preventing hemi-fusion/fusion to occur. We previously demonstrated that ARB inhibits membrane fusion of liposomes, we therefore favor this "membrane intoxication model" as it also explains the accumulation of HCV in endosomal compartments due to impaired fusion and cytosolic release. We recently proposed a similar mechanism of action for silibinin, a 1:1 mixture of flavonolignans silybin A and silybin B (Blaising et al., 2013). ARB would therefore constitute a potent broad spectrum antiviral agent able to hinder the entry of several viruses infecting their host cells by CME.

Acknowledgments

We thank C.M. Rice for Huh7.5 cells, J. Dubuisson for HCVpp plasmids and antibodies, C. Chamot, O. Duc and C. Lionnet for training and help with cell imaging (PLATIM, ENS Lyon), J.J. Blaising (CERN, Geneva) for expertise on statistical analyses and J. Klinghauf for eGFP-clathrin plasmid. E-I.P. is supported by FINOVI foundation and ANRS. S.B. was supported by the Chica and Heinz Schaller foundation (Germany) and the European Union Seventh Framework Program (FP7-PEOPLE-2012-CIG) under the grant agreement n°334336. J.B. is the recipient of a PhD grant from Cluster Infectiologie Région Rhône Alpes.

Appendix A. Supplementary data

Supplementary data associated with this article can be found, in the online version, at http://dx.doi.org/10.1016/j.antiviral.2013. 08.008.

References

Bartosch, B., Dubuisson, J., Cosset, F.L., 2003. Infectious hepatitis C virus pseudo-particles containing functional E1–E2 envelope protein complexes. J. Exp. Med. 197, 633–642.

Blaising, J., Lévy P.L., Gondeau, C., Phelip, C., Varbanov, M., Teissier, E., Ruggiero, F., Polyak, S.J., Oberlies, N.H., Ivanovic, T., Boulant, S., Pécheur, E.I., 2013. Silibinin inhibits hepatitis C virus entry into hepatocytes by hindering clathrin-dependent trafficking. Cell Microbiol. Nov;15(11); 1866-82.

Boriskin, Y.S., Pécheur, E.I., Polyak, S.J., 2006. Arbidol: a broad-spectrum antiviral that inhibits acute and chronic HCV infection. Virol. J. 3, 56.

Boriskin, Y.S., Leneva, I.A., Pécheur, E.I., Polyak, S.J., 2008. Arbidol: a broad-spectrum antiviral compound that blocks viral fusion. Curr. Med. Chem. 15, 997–1005.

Boulant, S., Kural, C., Zeeh, J.C., Ubelmann, F., Kirchhausen, T., 2011. Actin dynamics counteract membrane tension during clathrin-mediated endocytosis. Nat. Cell Biol. 13, 1124–1131.

Brooks, M.J., Sasadeusz, J.J., Tannock, G.A., 2004. Antiviral chemotherapeutic agents against respiratory viruses: where are we now and what's in the pipeline? Curr. Opin. Pulm. Med. 10, 197–203.

Brooks, M.J., Burtseva, E.I., Ellery, P.J., Marsh, G.A., Lew, A.M., Slepushkin, A.N., Crowe, S.M., Tannock, G.A., 2012. Antiviral activity of arbidol, a broad-spectrum drug for use against respiratory viruses, varies according to test conditions. J. Med. Virol. 84, 170–181.

Chai, H., Zhao, Y., Zhao, C., Gong, P., 2006. Synthesis and in vitro anti-hepatitis B virus activities of some ethyl 6-bromo-5-hydroxy-1H-indole-3-carboxylates. Bioorg. Med. Chem. 14, 911–917.

Cureton, D.K., Massol, R.H., Saffarian, S., Kirchhausen, T.L., Whelan, S.P., 2009. Vesicular stomatitis virus enters cells through vesicles incompletely coated with clathrin that depend upon actin for internalization. PLoS Pathog. 5, e1000394.

Delogu, I., Pastorino, B., Baronti, C., Nougairede, A., Bonnet, E., de Lamballerie, X., 2011. In vitro antiviral activity of arbidol against Chikungunya virus and characteristics of a selected resistant mutant. Antiviral Res. 90, 99–107.

Ehrlich, M., Boll, W., Van Oijen, A., Hariharan, R., Chandran, K., Nibert, M.L., Kirchhausen, T., 2004. Endocytosis by random initiation and stabilization of clathrin-coated pits. Cell 118, 591–605.

Haid, S., Pietschmann, T., Pécheur, E.I., 2009. Low pH-dependent hepatitis C virus membrane

fusion depends on E2 integrity, target lipid composition, and density of virus particles. J. Biol. Chem. 284, 17657–17667.
Leneva, I.A., Russell, R.J., Boriskin, Y.S., Hay, A.J., 2009. Characteristics of arbidol-resistant mutants of influenza virus: implications for the mechanism of anti-influenza action of arbidol. Antiviral Res. 81, 132–140.
Maginnis, M.S., Mainou, B.A., Derdowski, A., Johnson, E.M., Zent, R., Dermody, T.S., 2008. NPXY motifs in the beta1 integrin cytoplasmic tail are required for functional reovirus entry. J. Virol. 82, 3181–3191.
Martinez, C.G., Guinea, R., Benavente, J., Carrasco, L., 1996. The entry of reovirus into L cells is dependent on vacuolar proton-ATPase activity. J. Virol. 70, 576–579.
Pécheur, E.I., Lavillette, D., Alcaras, F., Molle, J., Boriskin, Y.S., Roberts, M., Cosset, F.L., Polyak, S.J., 2007. Biochemical mechanism of hepatitis C virus inhibition by the broad-spectrum antiviral arbidol. Biochemistry 46, 6050–6059.
Schulz, W.L., Haj, A.K., Schiff, L.A., 2012. Reovirus uses multiple endocytic pathways for cell entry. J. Virol. 86, 12665–12675.
Teissier, E., Penin, F., Pécheur, E.I., 2010. Targeting cell entry of enveloped viruses as an antiviral strategy. Molecules 16, 221–250.
Teissier, E., Zandomeneghi, G., Loquet, A., Lavillette, D., Lavergne, J.P., Montserret, R., Cosset, F.L., Bockmann, A., Meier, B.H., Penin, F., Pécheur, E.I., 2011. Mechanism of inhibition of enveloped virus membrane fusion by the antiviral drug arbidol. PLoS One 6, e15874.
Villalain, J., 2010. Membranotropic effects of arbidol, a broad anti-viral molecule, on phospholipid model membranes. J. Phys. Chem. B 114, 8544–8554.
Wakita, T., Pietschmann, T., Kato, T., Date, T., Miyamoto, M., Zhao, Z., Murthy, K., Habermann, A., Krausslich, H.G., Mizokami, M., Bartenschlager, R., Liang, T.J., 2005. Production of infectious hepatitis C virus in tissue culture from a cloned viral genome. Nat. Med. 11, 791–796.

Arbidol as a broad-spectrum antiviral: An update

Julie Blaising [a], Stephen J. Polyak [b,c], Eve-Isabelle Pécheur [a,⇑]
[a] CRCL, Inserm U1052, CNRS 5286, University of Lyon, Lyon, France
[b] Dept of Laboratory Medicine, University of Washington, Seattle, WA, USA
[c] Dept of Global Health, University of Washington, Seattle, WA, USA

Keywords:Arbidol, Influenza, Hepatitis C virus, Entry, Fusion, Antiviral therapy

Abstract

Arbidol (ARB) is a Russian-made small indole-derivative molecule, licensed in Russia and China for prophylaxis and treatment of influenza and other respiratory viral infections. It also demonstrates inhibitory activity against other viruses, enveloped or not, responsible for emerging or globally prevalent infectious diseases such as hepatitis B and C, gastroenteritis, hemorrhagic fevers or encephalitis. In this review, we will explore the possibility and pertinence of ARB as a broad-spectrum antiviral, after a careful examination of its physico-chemical properties, pharmacokinetics, toxicity, and molecular mechanisms of action. Recent studies suggest that ARB's dual interactions with membranes and aromatic amino acids in proteins may be central to its broad-spectrum antiviral activity. This could impact on the virus itself, and/or on cellular functions or critical steps in virus-cell interactions, thereby positioning ARB as both a direct-acting antiviral (DAA) and a host-targeting agent (HTA). In the context of recent studies in animals and humans, we will discuss the prospective clinical use of ARB in various viral infections.

⇑ Corresponding author. Address: UMR Inserm U1052/CNRS 5286, CRCL, 151 Cours Albert Thomas, 69424 Lyon Cedex 03, France. Tel.: +33 472681975. E-mail address: eve-isabelle.pecheur@inserm.fr (E.-I. Pécheur).

1. Introduction

Arbidol (ARB) has been administered for decades in Russia and China against influenza, with no major adverse effects reported. Its vast potential as a broad-spectrum antiviral agent, defined through in vitro and in vivo studies, lends hope for its clinical use against various infectious diseases that are at present not therapeutically controlled. However, evidence for beneficial effects in humans, especially in the perspective of long-term administration in chronic diseases, remains equivocal. This could be attributable to a relative lack of standardized animal studies and controlled clinical trials in healthy and infected subjects. In addition to influenza and pathogenic human respiratory viruses, ARB shows mainly in vitro inhibitory activity against the hepatitis B virus (HBV), hepatitis C virus (HCV), chikungunya virus (CHIKV), reovirus, Hantaan virus and coxsackie virus B5.

In this paper, we update current knowledge about ARB, linking its physico-chemical properties to its molecular mode of action, toxicity and possible pharmaceutical forms. We will outline recent studies on the molecular and cellular mechanisms by which ARB may inhibit several steps of viral life cycles, and discuss how ARB is emerging as both a direct-acting agent (DAA) and a host-targeting agent (HTA).

2. Overview of ARB: history, initial clinical studies in Russia and China, toxicity

ARB, or ethyl-6-bromo-4-[(dimethylamino)methyl]-5-hydroxy-1-methyl-2 [(phenylthio)methyl]-indole-3-carboxylate hydrochlo-ride monohydrate, is a small indole derivative (Fig. 1A). It is also called umifenovir. Its invention is attributed to a joint consortium of Russian scientists from the Chemical–Pharmaceutical Scientific Research Institute of Russia, the Scientific Research Institute of Medical Radiology in Obninsk and the Leningrad-Pasteur Scientific Research Institute for epidemiology and microbiology, some 40 years ago, as described in:

arbidol.net/robert-nikolaevich-glushkov.html arbidol.org/1973-4-arbidol-invented-WAY-To-THE DISCOVERY.pdf
arbidol.org/article1.html.

One of the first descriptions of its chemical synthesis was published in 1993 (Trofimov et al., 1993), and modified later on Miller and Bergeron (1994). The drug is manufactured by Moscow-based Masterlek™, a subsidiary of Pharmstandard Group (see below), and by Shijiazhuang No.4 Pharmaceutical™ in China (http://www.sjzsiyao.com/products_detail/&productId=46.html).

ARB has been marketed for 20 years in Russia and has been used since 2006 in China for the prophylaxis and treatment of human pulmonary diseases caused by influenza A and B viruses and other human pathogenic respiratory viruses, as reviewed in Boriskin et al. (2008), Brooks et al. (2004). It is also used to prevent flu epi-demics in poultry in China (Berendsen et al., 2012), and is available from Chinese companies specialized in animal health products, such as:

http://depond.b2bage.com/product-chemical-auxiliary-agent/ 1503414/arbidol-hydrochloride-pharmaceutical-raw-material.html

The first reports on the clinical efficacy of ARB were published in Russian in the 1990s, in groups of students and industrial work-ers during epidemics of influenza A and outbreaks of acute respira-tory diseases (Gagarinova et al., 1993; Obrosova-Serova et al., 1991). Later studies performed in servicemen reported the efficacy and cost-effectiveness of prophylactic or curative treatments of ARB against acute respiratory viral infections, where ARB was shown to decrease the febrile period (Shumilov et al., 2002; Shuster et al., 2004). When the information is available, the dura-tion of ARB treatment varies from 5 to 20 days.

Chinese clinical studies with similar design (patient inclusion criteria, ARB doses and duration of administration) point to a com-parable efficacy and tolerability of ARB (Wang et al., 2004). ARB efficacy compared well or even better with that of other commonly used antiviral molecules such as rimantadine (Roflual), oseltamivir (Tamiflu), ribavirin or interferon-alpha (Gatich et al., 2008; Kolobukhina et al., 2008, 2009; Leneva and Shuster, 2006). It potentiated the in vitro effect of rimantadine against influenza A and B viruses (Burtseva et al., 2007), enhanced the immunomodulatory properties of the anti-flu vaccine Vaxigrip , administered in a cohort of 125 elderly patients (Semenenko et al., 2005), and had a beneficial effects on flu in patients with another infectious immunodeficiency (Glushkov et al., 1999).

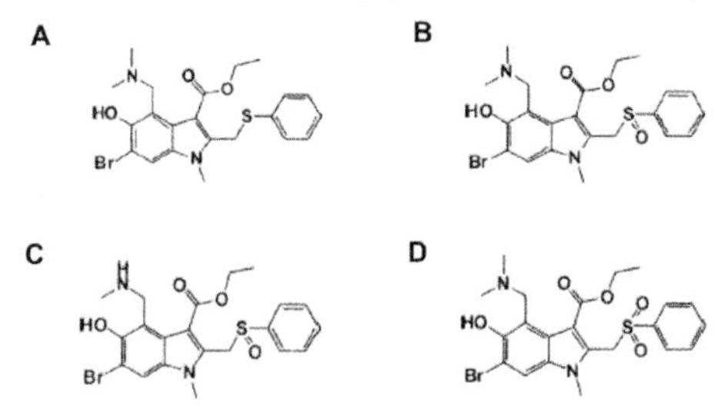

Fig. 1 Chemical structures of arbidol (A), sulfonyl-arbidol (B), and sulfinyl-arbidol (C). In D, structure of a prototypic aryl-thio-indole molecule, as synthesized by La Regina et al. (2013).

Most of these studies point to a dual pharmacological action of ARB: a specific effect on respiratory viruses and an immune-stimulating effect, with induction of serum interferon and activation of phagocytes. Studies have also been conducted in children suffering from flu and other acute viral respiratory diseases (Beliaev et al., 1996; Drinevskii et al., 1998). The latter study – and most documented one – was conducted on 158 children of 1–14 years old, infected with influenza A or B or both or with other respiratory viruses. Over a 5-day treatment, ARB was efficient at reducing the duration of infection and the occurrence of complications, and its immunomodulating action was again suggested. In 2002, Masterlek™, the company currently marketing ARB, sponsored a vast clinical trial conducted on 500 children from 6 to over 12 years old. ARB was given (i) either in prophylaxis twice a week for 3 weeks or once daily for 12 days; (ii) or in treatment thrice daily for 3 days. In all cases, ARB treatment led to a significant reduction of the duration of clinical signs, with no observed adverse effect or complications; see: http://arbidol.org/arbidol-childrens-study.pdf.

Interestingly, in studies comparing antivirals, most viral strains were sensitive to ARB, whereas several resistant variants were found with rimantadine (cf also the recent Iatsyshina et al., 2010;

L'vov et al., 2013) (see also Section 7.). Since 2004, ARB is also patented by Masterlek™ for its medici-nal use as an antiviral agent against atypical pneumonia induced by the severe acute respiratory syndrome coronavirus (SARS-CoV); see:
http://www.arbidol.org/arbidol-patent-2004-sars-russian.pdf

Most recently, a double-blind, randomized, placebo-controlled phase IV clinical trial has been launched by Pharmstandard/Mas-terlek™, to assess whether ARB is effective in the treatment and prophylaxis of flu and common cold:
http://clinicaltrials.gov/ct2/show/
NCT01651663?term=arbidol&rank=1.

Two dosages will be evaluated: 800 mg/day for 5 days, or 200 mg/day for 10 days. Completion of this study is expected in 2015.

Apart from this recent trial and in spite of an abundance of studies in the 1990s, the overall language barrier renders difficult the precise evaluation of the number of subjects enrolled per study, the way clinical trials were designed, and subsequent statistical analyses performed. Moreover, an official Russian site exists for arbidol (arbidol.ru), where more information could be collected; but no English translation is available.

As to studies specifically addressing ARB toxicity issues, initial literature is mostly in Russian, when available. Acute toxicity data report oral LD50s of 340–400 mg/kg in mice, and >3000 mg/kg in rats and guinea pigs:
http://img1.guidechem.com/msdspdf/131707-23-8.pdf; Glushkov, 1992.

These values are also reported elsewhere: http://arbidol.org/pre-1990-animal-human-test-results.pdf;

http://arbidol.org/rat.html; (Loginova et al., 2009; Shi et al., 2007). Administered intravenously, ARB exhibited LD_{50}s of 109 mg/kg in mice and 140 mg/kg in rats (Eropkin et al., 2009). On long-term per os administration of ARB in rats, guinea pigs, rabbits or dogs from 2 to over 6 months (with doses ranging from 25 to 125 mg/ kg), no pathological changes were observed in animals. These doses would roughly correspond to 10- to 50-fold the therapeutic doses in humans.

ARB is also reported not to induce embryo toxicity in pregnant female rats, nor alter the reproductive function of animals, over a 20 day-administration period of 500 mg/kg doses (http://arb-idol.org/rat.html). Recent data from a Chinese group showed a good tolerability of ARB administered to rats per os, at daily doses ranging from 80 to 320 mg/kg over a 4-week period (Wang et al., 2010). But in fact this study assessed the toxicity of a 1:2.5 combination of ARB with acetaminophen, which renders difficult to precisely evaluate the toxicity of each molecule individually. In healthy male volunteers receiving a single 200 mg-dose of ARB, an excellent tolerability was reported (Liu et al., 2009).

From these data, it appears that ARB is a well-tolerated mole-cule with a high therapeutic index, when administered on periods ranging from a few days to a month. To date, however, no studies have addressed the long-term administration of ARB, for example in the context of chronic infections.

3. ARB bioavailability, pharmacokinetics and metabolism

As an indole derivative, ARB is expected to be poorly soluble in aqueous media. This is of major repercussion on its bioavailability, forms of administration and pharmacokinetics. Efforts to improve ARB water solubility were undertaken, through the chemical grafting of acrylamide polymers to the ARB molecule (Eropkin et al., 2009). Antiviral properties of these complexes were maintained compared to the parent molecule. They also displayed a better in vitro pharmacological index than ARB, defined as IC_{50}/VIC_{50} (VIC, virus-inhibiting concentration). However these polymers were not further developed. ARB is soluble in hot glycerol, where it remains soluble down to 23 °C. It can then be diluted into aqueous media and administered in vitro or in vivo (Brooks et al., 2012). However no pharmacokinetic nor metabolite studies were performed from this mode of administration.

A very selective, sensitive and accurate method of detection of ARB from human plasma by high-pressure liquid chromatography was designed, and allowed to conclude that no interference existed between ARB and its expected metabolites (Metz et al., 1998). Studies based upon this HPLC method then evaluated the pharma-cokinetic parameters of ARB after oral or intravenous administra-tion in rats. Comparable plasma elimination half-lives ($t_{1/2}$) and maximum concentrations (C_{max}) were obtained for oral doses six times higher than those injected; however this was only performed on a small number of animals (Liu et al., 2007a). The drug is manufactured in Russia and China as tablets or capsules, each con-taining ARB as its active ingredient. Initial Russian studies in humans revealed that the main site of ARB metabolism is the liver. ARB was rapidly distributed in tissues and organs with maximal accumulation in liver (3.1% w/w), pituitary gland, kidneys, lympha-tic nodes and thyroid, adrenal gland, bone marrow, lungs, plasma, thymus and spleen (less than 1% each) (Glushkov, 1992); see:
http://www.chemeurope.com/en/encyclopedia/Arbidol.html.

Plasma C_{max} was reached within 1 h or 1.5 h after a 50 mg-or 100 mg-dose, respectively, and $t_{1/2}$ was between 17 and 21 h. About 40% of the total intake dose of ARB was excreted unchanged within 48 h via feces. More recent studies reported much shorter plasma C_{max} and $t_{1/2}$ in Chinese healthy volunteers, concluding that Russian and Chinese populations differed in ARB elimination rates (Liu et al., 2007b, 2009). However doses administered differed, and technological improvements, especially in detection sensitivity, might also explain such discrepancies. Single doses of 200 mg of ARB administered to healthy volunteers from dispersible tablets or capsules were found bioequivalent and well tolerated (Liu et al., 2009). Pharmacokinetics of oral single vs multiple doses of ARB were compared in healthy subjects, from plasma samples analyzed by HPLC (Metz et al., 1998; Sun et al., 2013). C_{max} increased linearly with the intake dose for single dose administrations, peaking at 2.16 μg/ml for a 800 mg-dose (Sun et al., 2013). ARB exhibited little accumulation with repeated doses, and the pharmacokinetic profile differed from that observed after single dosage.

Based on ARB's chemical structure, several metabolites can be predicted (Fig. 1A): oxidation at the sulfur atom, loss of the 4-(dimethylamino)methyle group and N-demethylation, conjuga-tion at the 5-hydroxyl moiety. In a pioneering study in rat urine, the formation of sulfone and sulfoxide forms was confirmed after HPLC, from an oral administration of an ARB/starch suspension (Anisimova et al., 1995). Glucuronide or sulfate conjugations were also observed at position 5, and after demethylation of the (dimethylamino)methyle group (see also Liu et al., 2012). In human urine, after administration of a single 300 mg-dose of ARB to healthy subjects, 17 metabolites could be identified, of which the major ones were ARB glucuronide and sulfoxide-ARB (or sulfi-nyl-ARB; Fig. 1B) glucuronide (Wang et al., 2008). Similar metabo-lites as identified in rats were observed.

ARB could also be glucuronidated in vitro, using purified human liver microsomes; this study also revealed that the microsomal (recombinant) UDP-glucuronosyl-transferase (UGT) 1A9 was the major UGT isoform involved in ARB glucuronidation (Song et al., 2013). Conversely, ARB was found to inhibit UGT1A9 (ibid.; Liu et al., 2013). Since UGT1A9 is involved in the metabolism of several drugs (e.g. acetominophen, diclofenac), potential drug-drug inter-actions that could lead to adverse effects should be carefully exam-ined if ARB is administered with other molecules. A more complete picture could be obtained from a study in healthy volunteers receiving a single oral dose of 200 mg ARB, where urine, feces and plasma metabolites were analyzed (Deng et al., 2013). Most of the metabolites were sulfoxidated, dimethylamine N-demethylated, glucuronide- or sulfate-conjugated. About 32.4% of the total intake dose of ARB was excreted unchanged via feces, as previously reported (Boriskin et al., 2008). Sulfinyl-ARB (Fig. 1B) was the major circulating component detected in plasma, followed by unmetabolized ARB, N-demethyl-sulfinyl-ARB and sulfonyl-ARB (Fig. 1C). Urine samples contained mainly glucuronide and sulfate conjugates. In vitro experiments using human liver, intestine and kidney microsomes, and recombinant enzymes, showed that ARB was metabolized by human microsomes from liver and intestines but not from kidney. In these organs, CYP3A4 was identified as a key metabolic enzyme of ARB.

Still, questions remain about the pharmacokinetic properties of ARB metabolites and their potential antiviral activity. The follow-ing parameters were reported (Deng et al., 2013): tmax for ARB and dimethylamine N-demethylated ARB were comparable (1.4 and 1.5 h, respectively), while it was much longer for sulfinyl-and sulfonyl-ARB (13 and 19 h). Plasma elimination half-lives ($t_{1/2}$) of all metabolites were longer than that of ARB (26.3, 25, 25.7 and 15.7 h for N-demethylated, sulfinyl-, sulfonyl-ARB and ARB, respectively). Exposure to metabolites is therefore greater than that to ARB, and the main metabolite, sulfinyl-ARB, is expected to accumulate on repeated ARB doses. Along these lines, sulfinyl-ARB was reported to contribute for some of the pharmacological activities associated with ARB, and sulfonyl-ARB could inhibit pro-tein kinase C ([IC50] = 7.78 μM) (Demin et al., 2010). Therefore the potency and duration effect for the agent may be underestimated by measuring only ARB concentrations.

It is also predictable, based upon in vitro data with microsomes, that some of the in vivo metabolites could occur in cell cultures, especially in studies addressing the antiviral effect of ARB on hepatotropic viruses using liver-derived cell lines. This could explain why ARB demonstrated greater efficacy under pre-incubation conditions, where metabolites could already be produced and exert specific effects (see below Section 4.). However, a recent study directly addressing the in vitro antiviral properties of sulfinyl-and sulfonyl-ARB against the Chikungunya alphavirus showed only moderate to weak activity as compared to that of the parent mol-ecule (Delogu et al., 2011). This was reinforced by the observation that pre-incubation of cells with ARB prior to infection did not improve antiviral effect, pointing to a minor role (if any) of ARB metabolites against Chikungunya infection, at least in vitro. In any case, further investigations will be necessary to: (i) understand the importance of metabolites in the efficacy and safety of ARB, due to their high plasma exposure and long elimination half-lives; (ii) assess their stability in circulation, tissue binding and storage properties.

4. Broad-spectrum antiviral activity of ARB

ARB has been shown to display antiviral in vitro and/or in vivo activity against a number of enveloped or non-enveloped RNA or DNA viruses, including influenza viruses A, B and C (Leneva et al., 2005), respiratory syncytial virus, SARS-CoV, adenovirus, parainfluenza type 5, poliovirus 1, rhinovirus 14, coxsackievirus B5, hantaan virus, Chikungunya virus, HBV and HCV [reviewed in Boriskin et al. (2008), Brooks et al. (2004, 2012), Liu et al. (2013a)] (see also Table 1).

4.1. Respiratory viruses

Numerous reports in Russian describe the antiviral potency of ARB against human or avian influenza A viruses, and notably the highly pathogenic H5N1 (Fediakina et al., 2005; Leneva and Shuster, 2006) and the pandemic 2009 H1N1 subtype (Fediakina et al., 2011). In vitro studies report IC50s in the 2.5–16 μM range, and state an effect of ARB comparable to that of ribavirin, but superior to that of rimantadine, with rimantadine-resistant strains sen-sitive to ARB (Burtseva et al., 2007; Romanovskaia et al., 2009; Leneva et al., 2010; Fediakina et al., 2011). A few studies state a potentiating effect of ARB and rimantadine (or amantadine) on influenza A and B viruses (Leneva et al., 2005; Burtseva et al., 2007). However adamantane antivirals are scarcely used against influenza viruses, due to low barrier to resistance. In these studies, accessible information does not allow to evaluate the stage of the viral life cycle targeted by ARB nor its mode of action. Shi and coworkers showed a greater inhibitory effect on influenza A H1N1 when ARB was added before infection or when it was pre-incubated with the virus (Shi et al., 2007), suggesting that membrane impregnation and/or metabolites could underlie ARB antiviral activity (see Section 6.). ARB demonstrated similar in vitro antiviral activity as the reference drug ribavirin (Virazole) against the respiratory syncytial virus (RSV), an enveloped virus of the Paramyxoviridae family (Leneva et al., 2002). ARB was most efficient when added before infection (Shi et al., 2007), with an IC50 of 16 μM.

Recently, Tannock and coworkers reported a potent antiviral activity of ARB on several virus families responsible of respiratory infections in animals and humans, in particular on influenza A H3N2 (IC50 12 μM), and the non-enveloped Picornaviridae poliovi-rus 1 and rhinovirus 14 (Brooks et al., 2012; see also Brooks et al., 2004). Concerning RSV, only a reduction in plaque size and not in number could be observed, hampering the estimation of an IC50. In this study, ARB was added to cells as an aqueous glycerol solution, instead of the classical dilution from DMSO in other studies (Leneva et al., 2002; Shi et al., 2007). This might explain the discrepancy of antiviral effect on RSV.

Table 1

Viruses against which ARB has demonstrated antiviral activity. Virion type: E, enveloped; NE, non-enveloped. References in bold report animal studies of ARB antiviral activity. See text for details and abbreviations.

Family	Virus	Virion type	In vitro IC50 (μM)	In vivo (mg/kg/day)	DAA/HTA	References
Orthomyxoviridae	Influenza	E	2.5–16 A/H3N2 12 B 13.3	A/H3N2 2–50 A/H1N1 100 A/H1N1 90–180 A 15–30	Both	Brooks et al. (2012), Fediakina et al. (2005, 2011), Leneva and Shuster (2006), Leneva et al. (2010), Liu et al. (2013b), Loginova et al. (2008), Shi et al. (2007)
Paramyxoviridae	RSV	E	16	–	nd/HTA	Shi et al. (2007)
			no IC50	10–50	nd/HTA	Brooks et al. (2012)
Picornaviridae	Poliovirus 1	NE	0.41	–	nd/HTA	Brooks et al. (2012)
	Rhinovirus 14	NE	12.2	–	nd/HTA	idem
	Coxsackie B5	NE	5	50	Both	Zhong et al. (2009)
Bunyaviridae	Hantaan	E	2	5–20	Both	Deng et al. (2009), Wei et al. (2013)
Rhabdoviridae	VSV	E	14	–	nd/HTA	Blaising et al. (2013)
Reoviridae	Reovirus T1L	NE	10	–	nd/HTA	Blaising et al. (2013)
Togaviridae	Chikungunya	E	12.2	–	not DAA/HTA	Delogu et al. (2011)
Hepadnaviridae	HBV	E	DNA replic 43 HBsAg 90	–	nd/HTA	Zhao et al. (2006)
Flaviviridae	HCV	E	2–11.3	–	Both	Blaising et al. (2013), Boriskin et al. (2006, 2008), Haid et al. (2009), Pécheur et al. (2007), Teissier et al. (2011)

ARB also displayed an inhibitory effect on the coxsackievirus B5, another member of the Picornaviridae family responsible for a vari-ety of pathologies including respiratory infections, myocarditis or encephalitis (Zhong et al., 2009). ARB was most active on the virus itself (virucidal test) or when added after infection, through the inhibition of late stages of viral replication. Indeed it was shown to prevent the viral RNA synthesis in a dose-dependent manner, with maximal effect obtained at 5 μM.

One study in Russian describes in vitro antiviral activity of ARB against the SARS-CoV, when added after viral infection and at high concentration (95 μM) (Khamitov et al., 2008). Depending on the cell type, ARB CC50 was reported to vary between 20 and 200 μM (e.g. Boriskin et al., 2006; Brancato et al., 2013; Brooks et al., 2012; Shi et al., 2007). The dose exhibiting anti-SARS-CoV activity may likely be cytotoxic.

Studies conducted on mouse-adapted flu models showed that ARB was effective when administered orally at doses from 15 to 30 mg/kg (Loginova et al., 2008; Leneva et al., 2010), or up to 100 mg/kg (Shi et al., 2007), especially when given in prophylaxis before infection. Extrapolated to humans, these doses would corre-spond to 1–6 g per day, not evaluated clinically in terms of safety.

Recently, ARB was found to be effective in vivo against two influenza A H1N1 strains, responsible for seasonal or pandemic flu (Liu et al., 2013b). Reductions in lung viral titers and lesions were observed for oral doses of 90–180 mg/kg/day, and secretion of lung and macrophage cytokines was modulated, indicating an inhibitory effect of ARB on virus-induced inflammation. However, no effect on interferon-alpha was observed, in line with (Brooks et al., 2012) but contrary to initial reports (Glushkov, 1992). Brooks et al. (2012) reported a minor effect of ARB on flu A-infected mice at doses from 2 to 50 mg/kg/day. Discrepancies between results from different groups might come from: (i) bioavailability issues, due to differences in solvents used to solubilize ARB (DMSO vs glycerol); (ii) animal models of flu, using viruses and viral strains adapted or not adapted to mice; (iii) doses administered to animals. However, an overall anti-flu effect of ARB in vivo seems apparent.

Mice with RSV-induced pneumonia were responsive to ARB at 10–50 mg/kg/day doses, with an observable but not significant reduction in lung infectious titers as compared to untreated ani-mals (Brooks et al., 2012). While this study points to a potential promising effect of ARB against RSV in vivo, the limited of global studies addressing the effect of ARB against RSV should invite moderation and a call for additional studies.

One study addressed the antiviral effect of ARB in mice infected with the coxsackievirus B5 (Zhong et al., 2009). Mice developed interstitial pneumonia and myocarditis, and some received ARB orally for 6 days. At a dose of 50 mg/kg, the drug prolonged survival and reduced viral propagation in lungs and heart. Although this result completes the picture of the broad-spectrum antiviral activity of ARB, it must again be taken with caution, since it is the sole study on this virus, conducted on a small number of ani-mals and with a high dose of ARB.

4.2. Viruses causing hemorrhagic fever and encephalitis

Recently, Chinese studies demonstrated antiviral activity of ARB against the Hantaan virus, an enveloped virus from the Bunyaviri-dae family (Deng et al., 2009; Wei et al., 2013), causing an often lethal hemorrhagic fever with renal syndrome (HFRS). In vitro, ARB was more efficient when added before infection, with an IC50 in the 2 μM range. A direct virucidal effect was noted only for ARB concentrations over 15 μM. In vivo, it was able to increase the survival rate, reduce histopathological changes and viral loads in the lethal model of intracranially-infected suckling mice. Also, serum levels of TNF-alpha were modulated. Since these studies were performed by only one research group, with a limited num-ber of animals, they should be reproduced by others before con-cluding to a beneficial effect of ARB against hantavirus infection. However ARB efficacy compared well in vivo with that of ribavirin, the reference treatment for such a disease (Wei et al., 2013).

Viruses from the Rhabdoviridae family are known to induce neu-rological disorders, encephalitis or, more recently reported, hemor-rhagic fever (Grard et al., 2012). The only study addressing the effect of ARB against a virus of this family was conducted in our laboratory on the vesicular stomatitis virus (VSV) (Blaising et al., 2013). This enveloped RNA virus mainly infects cattle and pigs, causing oral lesions, anorexia and lethargy. ARB was shown to inhi-bit in vitro VSV infection in a very similar concentration range as that already shown to affect influenza A or RSV infection [IC50 of 14 (Blaising et al., 2013), 12 (Brooks et al., 2012) or 16 μM (Shi et al., 2007), respectively]. Again, ARB displayed optimal antiviral activity when incubated with cells before infection.

4.3. Non-enveloped Reoviridae

This family of double-stranded RNA viruses comprises animal and human pathogens, such as the rotavirus, a major agent of gastroenteritis in children. We recently addressed the potential of ARB against the mammalian reovirus T1L strain (Blaising et al., 2013). This virus is a prototypic member of the Orthoreovirus genus, which infects a wide variety of host species without causing a significant pathology in humans. In spite of this, reovirus has pro-ven to be a useful model for studying viral pathogenesis. In vitro, ARB inhibited reovirus infection in the 10 μM range, but interest-ingly, did not exert any effect on infectious subvirion particles (ISVPs), intermediates of reovirus infection (Chandran et al., 2002) that could also directly infect cells via a different entry mechanism from that of reovirus (Martinez et al., 1996). This points to the molecular mechanisms of action of ARB (detailed in Section 6.).

4.4. Chikungunya virus (CHIKV) infection

This alphavirus is an enveloped single-stranded RNA virus from the Togaviridae family, loosely related to Flaviviridae (see below HCV). It is responsible for recent outbreaks of a rheumatological disease. Some neurological complications were described, together with meningo-encephalitis. ARB demonstrated potent in vitro activity against CHIKV infection (Delogu et al., 2011). ARB did not show virucidal activity, contrary to data on respiratory viruses (Shi et al., 2007; Zhong et al., 2009), and displayed the highest effi-ciency when preincubated with cells 24 h before infection (IC50 7.5 μM). In this study, the main metabolites sulfinyl- and sulfonyl-ARB were assayed and exhibited only weak antiviral activity, with IC50s > 55 μM. ARB activity was not improved when a 12 h-preincubation with cells was performed, suggesting that metabolites or degradation products are not responsible for ARB antiviral action. Taken together, these results suggest an interfer-ence of the parent molecule ARB with early steps of the viral life cycle, such as cell binding and entry.

4.5. Hepatitis viruses

ARB and derivatives demonstrated in vitro efficiency against the hepatitis B virus (HBV), an enveloped DNA virus from the Hepadnaviridae family (Chai et al., 2006; Zhao et al., 2006). ARB prevented HBV DNA replication with an IC50 of 45 μM, and reduced the pro-duction of the virion surface antigen HBsAg at 90 μM; however the 50% cytotoxic concentration was 140 μM, suggesting that inhibitory concentrations are most likely cytotoxic. This work will be further discussed below in the section structure/activity relationship (SAR; Section 5.).

We showed that ARB exerts in vitro antiviral activity against the hepatitis C virus (HCV) (reviewed in Boriskin et al. (2008)), a member of the Flaviviridae family of enveloped viruses. More specifically, ARB was most efficient when incubated with cells before infection and left during infection (Pécheur et al., 2007). As already shown with other viruses, ARB also displayed virucidal activity (Haid et al., 2009; Pécheur et al., 2007). In the 10 μM range, ARB inhibited HCV entry, fusion in in vitro and in cellulo studies (Blaising et al., 2013; Haid et al., 2009; Teissier et al., 2011), and replication on longer times of cell treatment (Boriskin et al., 2006; Sellitto et al., 2010). However, as previously reported in the case of influenza A infection in vivo (Brooks et al., 2012), ARB was not found to induce interferon antiviral responses in vitro against HCV (Boriskin et al., 2006). From these studies, ARB molecular mechanisms of action were proposed (see Section 6 below).

5. ARB structure–activity relationship (SAR)

Several studies aimed at gaining a better understanding of the structural features of ARB important for its broad antiviral activity, improving ARB therapeutic index, or identifying novel lead compounds active against emergent viruses. Compounds derived from the chemical structure of ARB were synthesized and assayed against various influenza A and B viruses (Brancato et al., 2013). The amine in position 4 and the hydroxyl moiety in position 5 were found important for ARB antiviral action, whereas the presence or absence of Br in position 6 had little effect (see Fig. 1A). Insertion of a methyl group between the indole ring and 5-hydroxyl consider-ably increased antiviral potency of the resulting compound. This molecule was shown to directly bind HA2, with a greater affinity than ARB.

The presence or absence of the 6-Bromo group had also no influence on HBV or HCV infections (Sellitto et al., 2010; Zhao et al., 2006). More specifically, the introduction of particular azote-based heterocyclic groups at position 4 improved anti-HBV activity (Zhao et al., 2006), while it had little effect against HCV (Sellitto et al., 2010). Replacement of the S-phenyl group at posi-tion 2 by a phenyl-sulfonyl decreased the cytotoxicity and increased the anti-HBV activity of the compound (Chai et al., 2006; Zhao et al., 2006), while removal of this group was without any influence against HCV (Sellitto et al., 2010). The 5-hydroxy group was found dispensable against HCV. Thus, it appears that different substituents of the ARB molecule play a role in the antivi-ral activity, depending on the virus considered, the cellular model used and the test conditions.

The combination of in vitro, in cellulo and in silico analyses will help refine the SAR of ARB. In particular, in silico molecular docking studies allowed the precise identification of amino-acid(s) involved in ARB (or derivative) interaction with HA2 (Nasser et al., 2013). Also, three-dimensional quantitative SAR (3D-QSAR) helped design novel anti-HBV compounds based upon a 5-hydroxy-1H-indole-3-carboxylate skeleton, and predict their antiviral potency (Chai et al., 2011). This type of approach is also now conceivable to study the potential interactions of ARB with HCV envelope glycoproteins and clarify structural requirements for antiviral activity, since the 3D-structure of HCV E2 has recently been released (Kong et al., 2013).

6. Molecular mechanisms of ARB antiviral action

ARB's broad-spectrum antiviral activity suggests that the molecule acts on common critical step(s) of virus-cell interactions. Evidence indicates that ARB directly exerts a virucidal effect, and can then be considered as a direct-acting antiviral (DAA). Most studies also report an effect of ARB on one or several stages of the viral life cycle, such as cell entry (attachment, internalization) and replication. ARB could therefore also act as a host-targeting agent (HTA). In the following section, we will examine the mecha-nisms by which ARB could exert such dual antiviral activity (recapitulated in Table 1).

6.1. ARB binds to both lipids and protein residues

ARB is an indole-based hydrophobic molecule susceptible to formation of supramolecular arrangements through aromatic stacking interactions with selective amino-acid residues of proteins (phenylalanine, tyrosine, tryptophan). By liquid-state NMR analysis, we showed that ARB displays interfacial properties and intercalates in the shallow layer above the glycerol backbone of phospholipids (Teissier et al., 2011). It is even conceivable that ARB could locally become more concentrated in viral or cellular membranes.

It was also shown that ARB interacts with aromatic residues within the viral glycoprotein involved in membrane interactions and destabilization necessary for fusion, aka the fusion protein (Leneva et al., 2009 for influenza hemagglutinin; Teissier et al., 2011 for HCV E2). This could therefore underlie the virucidal (DAA) effect of ARB, interacting with the viral lipid envelope and/or with key residues within structural proteins of virions (required for cellular receptor/captor recognition and/or membrane fusion). This effect has been described for enveloped [influenza A H1N1 virus (Shi et al., 2007); Hantaan virus (Deng et al., 2009); HCV (Haid et al., 2009; Pécheur et al., 2007)] and non-enveloped viruses [coxsackie virus B5 (Zhong et al., 2009)], consistent with ARB's dual physico-chemical properties. ARB could also locally impair viral attachment to cell plasma membrane by stabilizing the membrane, and/or by masking key residues in a viral protein involved in receptor recognition, in a sort of DAA + HTA effect. This would have consequences on viral entry.

As shown by fluorescence spectroscopy and surface plasmon resonance analyses, ARB affinity for lipid membranes is even more pronounced at acidic pH, the optimal pH for the fusion step of several enveloped viruses, influenza viruses and HCV in particular (Fig. 2) (Haid et al., 2009; Pécheur et al., 2007; Teissier et al., 2010, 2011). This interaction with phospholipids may perturb

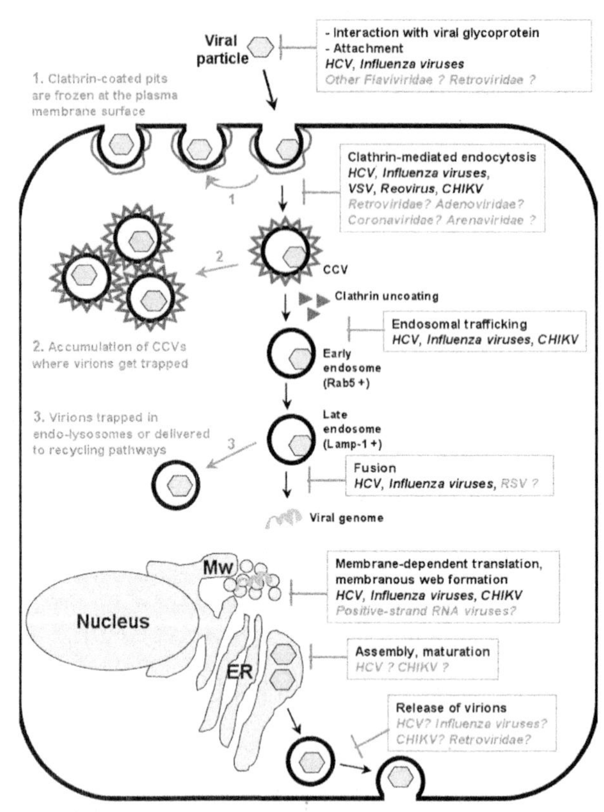

Fig. 2. Broad-spectrum activity of ARB and its molecular mechanisms of action at the cellular level. The different steps of the viral life cycle inhibited by ARB are indicated in blue boxes. Potential effect of ARB on other viruses or families of viruses are mentioned in orange. Blue arrows and text indicate the consequences of ARB on cellular pathways and virions. For clarity and regarding current knowledge about the molecular mechanisms of ARB, we only show the clathrin-dependent endocytosis pathway. MW, membranous web, ER, endoplasmic reticulum.

membrane fluidity, thereby rendering the lipid bilayer less prone to fusion. Inhibition of viral entry and membrane fusion occurred in the 10 μM range, in agreement with ARB affinity for membranes and the concentration range achieved in healthy volunteers (Sun et al., 2013).

Mechanistically, the dual binding capacity of ARB to lipids and proteins might also underlie alterations of protein/protein and/or protein/lipid interactions at other stages of the viral life cycles, such as replication, assembly and budding. For a number of viruses, in particular in the Flaviviridae family, replication occurs in a subcellular compartment called the membranous web (Heaton and Randall, 2011; Moradpour et al., 2007). The membranous web is an emanation of the endoplasmic reticulum induced by viral proteins such as HCV NS4B (Gouttenoire et al., 2010; Romero-Brey et al., 2012). Since the web is created and maintained through interactions between viral and cellular proteins and lipids, it is plausible that ARB could impair viral replication through its ability to bind proteins and lipids. Concerning viral assembly and budding, intracellular membranes are obligate partners of nucleo-capsids during packaging of enveloped viruses, and for the secretion of newly assembled viral particles. In the case of HCV, viral assembly is concomitant to the assembly of lipoproteins, giving rise to lipo-viro particles (Bartenschlager et al., 2011). ARB could therefore interfere with these processes through its physico-chemical dual interactions with lipids and proteins.

6.2. ARB inhibition of viral entry

Recently, we provided molecular details of how ARB inhibits virus entry into target cells, in a study based on live-cell confocal imaging, using HCV as a model of an enveloped virus (Blaising et al., 2013) (Fig. 2). First, ARB was found to drastically impede virion attachment to cell plasma membrane. ARB subsequently impaired the release of clathrin-coated pits (CCPs) from the plasma membrane, resulting in a slowing of clathrin-coated vesicle (CCV) intracellular trafficking. The net result was an intracellular accumulation of CCVs containing trapped virions. ARB was also shown to affect clathrin-mediated endocytosis (CME) by impeding dyn-amin-2-induced membrane scission, and thereby CCP formation. Lastly, ARB inhibited fusion between endocytic vesicles and endo-somes and hindered viral intracellular trafficking. Virions were not properly delivered to Rab5-positive endosomal compartments where fusion occurs and/or Rab5 was not recruited to virion-containing vesicles. As a result, fusion was greatly impaired and virions trafficked to endo-lysosomal Lamp-1-positive compart-ments for degradation.

Overall, the data suggest that ARB's dual interactions with lipids and proteins may alter several aspects of intracellular trafficking with and maturation in endosomal compartments. ARB may impede the recruitment and/or disassembly of machineries required for proper endosomal trafficking and viral entry. Thus, ARB inhibition of key actors of intracellular trafficking may be a likely explanation of its broad-spectrum antiviral activity (Table 1, Fig. 2), and suggest that ARB acts as an HTA.

In most studies, ARB exerted a maximal antiviral effect when used before infection, indicating an activity on early stages of viral infection and/or the requirement for ARB to impregnate cells. In the current state of the literature, ARB was shown to be active against viruses that enter cells by routes requiring at least one of these features: acidification, Rab5, dynamin-2, actin. Reovirus, VSV and HCV hijack CME (respectively: Boulant et al., 2013; Johannsdottir et al., 2009; Meertens et al., 2006), HBV also most likely enters via this pathway (Yan et al., 2012). CHIKV entry is mainly achieved via CME (Leung et al., 2011), but alternative clath-rin-independent pathways have been described, dependent upon pH, dynamin-2, Rab5 and actin cytoskeleton integrity (Bernard et al., 2010).

Viruses such as influenza or hantaan can enter through clathrin-dependent and -independent endocytotic pathways that have acid-ification in common (reviewed in Mercer and Helenius (2009), Lozach et al. (2010)). RSV entry is achieved by macropinocytosis and, as shown for HCV, the intracellular trafficking of virions is Rab5-dependent (Krzyzaniak et al., 2013). In the Picornaviridae family, group B coxsackieviruses entry in epithelial cells occurs via a complex process, combining caveolin-dependent endocytosis with features of macropinocytosis such as dependence upon Rab5 (Coyne et al., 2007). Also in this family, poliovirus 1 relies on an actin- and tyrosine kinase-dependent endocytic pathway to invade its target cells (Brandenburg et al., 2007), and rhinovirus 14 entry is pH-dependent and likely achieved by macropinocytosis (Khan et al., 2010). Concerning SARS-CoV entry, the only consensus fea-ture is its dependence on acidification in internal cell compart-ments (Inoue et al., 2007; Wang et al., 2008).

Apart from lipid membranes, it is therefore conceivable that ARB acts on several cellular targets common to the life cycle of var-ious viruses. Studies directly addressing ARB as an HTA and its interactions with proteins of intracellular trafficking are not available at present, but from our work with HCV, Rab5, dynamin-2 and elements of the clathrin coat could be potential targets (Blaising et al., 2013). It is also conceivable that elements of the cytoskeleton could be targeted; indeed, molecules based on an aryl-thio-indole skeleton (Fig. 1D), closely related to ARB chemically, are inhibitors of tubulin polymerization, and thereby potent anticancer agents (La Regina et al., 2013).

6.3. ARB inhibition of viral fusion

ARB was reported to inhibit influenza- and HCV-mediated membrane fusion (Leneva et al., 2009; Teissier et al., 2011). In vitro studies showed that ARB increases the stability of the influenza virus hemagglutinin (HA) and hinders low pH structural reorgani-zations necessary for HA to adopt its fusiogenic conformation, thus blocking infection at the viral fusion step (Leneva et al., 2009; see also below Section 7.). Concerning HCV, fusion inhibition is dose-dependent but does not depend on the HCV genotype or on the lipid composition of target membranes (liposomes); it predominantly prevails at low pH (Boriskin et al., 2006; Haid et al., 2009; Pécheur et al., 2007; Teissier et al., 2011). ARB was found to directly interact with peptides from the HCV E2 glycoprotein (Teissier et al., 2011) and within a pocket of the influenza HA2 subunit of hemagglutinin (Nasser et al., 2013), thereby exerting its effect as a DAA. Interestingly, these peptides and pocket contain aromatic residues such as tyrosines and tryptophans, which could engage in aromatic stacking interactions with ARB molecules, as described above. ARB may therefore inhibit fusion by impairing conformational changes in viral fusion proteins during initiation of fusion (DAA activity) and by increasing membrane rigidity, ren-dering membranes refractory to the destabilization that is required for fusion (HTA activity).

6.4. ARB inhibition of viral replication, assembly and budding

ARB was shown to inhibit HCV replication in replicon systems, i.e. a cell culture context where virus replicates without any pro-duction of infectious viral particles (Boriskin et al., 2006; Sellitto et al., 2010). A progressive decline in both viral protein and RNA expression was observed in ARB-treated cells, and cells could be cured of replicating viral RNA after 10 weeks of ARB treatment (Boriskin et al., 2006). Since HCV modulates lipid metabolism (Bassendine et al., 2013) and creates a lipid-rich internal mem-brane environment favorable for virus replication (i.e. the mem-branous web), ARB could therefore impregnate these membranes to impede the formation and maintenance of the membranous web and in turn viral replication.

CHIKV replication takes place in the host cell cytoplasm and is associated with cytoplasmic membrane alterations (Solignat et al., 2009). Replication complexes are attached to the membrane of modified endosomes and lysosomes to form organelles charac-teristic of alphavirus replication called type 1 cytopathic vacuoles. These vacuoles consist in vesicles of 0.6–2.0 microns in diameter harboring numerous spherules (Grimley et al., 1968), which are posi-tive for lysosomal markers (Kujala et al., 2001). The vacuoles produce viral RNA until cell death. As already described for HCV, lipid bilayers are therefore essential for CHIKV replication. It is thus plausible that ARB may also impede the formation and stability of these vacuoles, thereby perturbing CHIKV replication.

In the absence of studies aimed at addressing the potential interactions between ARB and cellular proteins involved in viral replication, one cannot exclude that such interactions might occur, as already suggested at the viral entry/maturation stage. To date, no report has been made concerning an effect of ARB on viral assembly; however, further investigations are still needed to address this question directly. Concerning viral budding, a recent study supports the notion that ARB could inhibit influenza virus egress because viral RNAs accumulate in cells at later stages of infection (Brooks et al., 2012). ARB impregnation of cellular membranes and/or the targeting of proteins involved in intracellular trafficking that relate to viral morphogenesis/budding could again underlie this observation.

7. Viral resistance to ARB

In spite of its usage in Russia and China for several years in flu, ARB does not seem to generate a high degree of viral resistance. Epidemic strains of influenza A/H1N1 and A/H3N2 isolated in Russia in 2008–2009 revealed resistance to oseltamivir and/or rimantadine, but were all sensitive to ARB (Burtseva et al., 2009). The 2009 pandemic swine influenza A/H1N1 was found largely resistant to rimantadine, but had retained its sensitivity to oseltamivir (Tamiflu) and ARB (Iatsyshina et al., 2010). In 2011–2012, influenza A/H3N2 and B viruses were found to be the cause of a vast epidemic in Russia; all tested strains were sensitive to oseltamivir, zanamivir (Relenza) and arbidol, but resistant to rimantadine (L'vov et al., 2013).

However resistance to ARB of various strains of influenza viruses has been reported, in particular in a population of influenza B (Burtseva et al., 2007). In a study aimed at understanding the anti-influenza mechanism of action of ARB, Leneva and colleagues isolated seven viral mutants from the influenza A/H7N7 "Wey-bridge" strain, that were refractory to ARB doses above 38 lM (Leneva et al., 2009). All mutants exhibited a single mutation in the HA2 subunit of the influenza hemagglutinin, the subunit involved in membrane fusion. This translated functionally into a 0.2-unit increase in the pH required to induce HA2 conformational changes. ARB was found to directly interact with HA2, thereby increasing its stability to pH and impeding fusion in endosomes during virus infection. Using an elegant proteomic approach, this interaction was further investigated by Nasser and coworkers, and found confined to one peptide encompassing HA2 residues 104–120. This region contains the ARB already identified mutation resistance K117R (Leneva et al., 2009; Nasser et al., 2013). Taken together, these data reveal that resistance of influenza viruses to ARB mainly arises from mutations in the HA2 fusion protein, con-sistent with ARB antiviral activity related to membrane fusion.

Addressing ARB antiviral mechanism of action against CHIKV, Delogu and coworkers isolated a mutant virus adapted to ARB at 56 μM (Delogu et al., 2011). This virus was characterized by a single mutation in the E2 viral envelope glycoprotein, in a region most likely involved in cell-surface receptor recognition, and maybe indirectly to membrane fusion. Clearly, additional studies on ARB resistance in the context of other viral infections are warranted.

8. Conclusion and perspectives

In conclusion, the broad-spectrum activity of ARB may arise through duality of function: a capacity to interact with both membranes and with viral and/or cellular proteins. ARB therefore has features of both a DAA and a HTA. These interactions would impede cellular processes and pathways that are hijacked by several viruses to infect their host cells. Regarding HCV, we have shown that ARB inhibits most steps of HCV entry, from attachment to internalization, until the final step of membrane fusion. ARB also inhibits HCV replication, which may arise via alteration of intracel-lular membrane-protein structures essential for intracellular trafficking (e.g. clathrin coat components, elements of the cytoskel-eton) and virus replication (e.g. membranous web), and could hinder membrane rearrangements necessary for the viral budding step. The broad-spectrum activity and the cellular mechanisms affected by ARB are summarized in Fig. 2. Through these effects, ARB could display an antiviral activity on viruses that hijack similar cellular pathways or have overlapping life cycles. In particular, endocytosis is used by several viruses and viral families including human immunodeficiency virus (von Kleist et al., 2011), Adenoviridae, Arenaviridae, Coronaviridae, Togaviridae to achieve productive infection (Table 1). Moreover, all positive-strand RNA viruses of eukaryotes are known to reorganize intracellular membranes to create specific virus replication organelles. For these reasons, efforts should be pursued in order to determine the potential inhibitory effect of ARB on a large class of viruses. A better under-standing of its molecular mechanisms of action would also contribute to refine the conditions at which it could be given in long-term regimens against chronic infections (e.g. hepatitis B or C). Indeed current data on toxicity issues are insufficient to evaluate the safety of ARB in chronic administration. Nevertheless, most studies point to a good tolerability of this molecule. In the present state of our knowledge, ARB could therefore constitute a cost-effective pharmacological approach, affordable for emerging countries in urgent need for effective antiviral therapies.

Acknowledgments

We thank Steeve Boulant for his invaluable contribution to live-cell imaging of HCV infection in Blaising et al., 2013. J.B. is the recipient of a doctoral Grant from the Rhône-Alpes region (ARC 1 Santé), and E-I. P. is supported by ANRS (Agence Nationale pour la Recherche sur le SIDA et les hépatites virales).

References

Anisimova, O.S., Frolova, L.V., Chistyakov, V.V., Ermachenkov, I.A., Golovanova, I.V., Zotova, S.A., Pleshkova, A.P., Yadrovskaya, V.A., Sheinker, Y.N., 1995. Study of metabolism of the antiviral drug arbidol by mass spectrometry, thin-layer and high-performance liquid chromatography. Pharm. Chem. J. 29, 78–82.

Bartenschlager, R., Penin, F., Lohmann, V., André, P., 2011. Assembly of infectious hepatitis C virus particles. Trends Microbiol. 19, 95–103.

Bassendine, M.F., Sheridan, D.A., Bridge, S.H., Felmlee, D.J., Neely, R.D., 2013. Lipids and HCV. Semin. Immunopathol. 35, 87–100.

Beliaev, A.L., Burtseva, E.I., Slepushkin, A.N., Beliaeva, N.A., et al., 1996. Arbidole – a new drug for prevention of influenza and acute viral respiratory infections in children [Russian]. Vestn. Ross. Akad. Med. Nauk. 8, 34–37.

Berendsen, B.J., Wegh, R.S., Essers, M.L., Stolker, A.A., Weigel, S., 2012. Quantitative trace analysis of a broad range of antiviral drugs in poultry muscle using column-switch liquid chromatography coupled to tandem mass spectrometry. Anal. Bioanal. Chem. 402, 1611–1623.

Bernard, E., Solignat, M., Gay, B., Chazal, N., Higgs, S., Devaux, C., Briant, L., 2010. Endocytosis of chikungunya virus into mammalian cells: role of clathrin and early endosomal compartments. PLoS ONE 5, e11479.

Blaising, J., Lévy, P.L., Polyak, S.J., Stanifer, M., Boulant, S., Pécheur, E.I., 2013. Arbidol inhibits viral entry by interfering with clathrin-dependent trafficking. Antiviral Res. 100, 215–219.

Boriskin, Y.S., Leneva, I.A., Pécheur, E.I., Polyak, S.J., 2008. Arbidol: a broad-spectrum antiviral compound that blocks viral fusion. Curr. Med. Chem. 15, 997–1005.

Boriskin, Y.S., Pécheur, E.I., Polyak, S.J., 2006. Arbidol: a broad-spectrum antiviral that inhibits acute and chronic HCV infection. Virol. J. 3, 56.

Boulant, S., Stanifer, M., Kural, C., Cureton, D.K., Massol, R., Nibert, M.L., Kirchhausen, T., 2013. Similar uptake but different trafficking and escape routes of reovirus virions and ISVPs imaged in polarized MDCK cells. Mol. Biol. Cell 24, 1196– 1207.

Brancato, V., Peduto, A., Wharton, S., et al., 2013. Design of inhibitors of influenza virus membrane fusion: synthesis, structure-activity relationship and in vitro antiviral activity of a novel indole series. Antiviral Res. 99, 125–135.

Brandenburg, B., Lee, L.Y., Lakadamyali, M., Rust, M.J., Zhuang, X., Hogle, James M., Hogle, J.M., 2007. Imaging poliovirus entry in live cells. PLoS Biol. 5 (7), e183.

Brooks, M.J., Burtseva, E.I., Ellery, P.J., Marsh, G.A., Lew, A.M., Slepushkin, A.N., Crowe, S.M., Tannock, G.A., 2012. Antiviral activity of arbidol, a broad-spectrum drug for use against respiratory viruses, varies according to test conditions. J. Med. Virol. 84, 170–181.

Brooks, M.J., Sasadeusz, J.J., Tannock, G.A., 2004. Antiviral chemotherapeutic agents against respiratory viruses: where are we now and what's in the pipeline? Curr. Opin. Pulmonary Med. 10, 197–203.

Burtseva, E.I., Shevchenko, E.S., Leneva, I.A., Merkulova, L.N., Oskerko, T.A., Shliapnikova, O.V., Zaplatnikov, A.L., Shuster, A.M., Slepushkin, A.N., 2007. Rimantadine and arbidol sensitivity of influenza viruses that caused epidemic
morbidity rise in Russia in the 2004–2005 season [Russian]. Vopr. Virusol. 52, 24–29.

Burtseva, E.I., Shevchenko, E.S., Beliakova, N.V., Oskerko, T.A., Kolobukhina, L.V., Merkulova, L.N., Vartanian, R.V., Prilipov, A.G., Rotanov, M., Zaplatnikov, A.L., 2009. Monitoring of the sensitivity of epidemic influenza virus strains isolated in Russia to etiotropic chemical agents [Russian]. Vopr. Virusol. 54, 24–28.

Chai, H., Zhao, Y., Zhao, C., Gong, P., 2006. Synthesis and in vitro anti-hepatitis B virus activities of some ethyl 6-bromo-5-hydroxy-1H-indole-3-carboxylates. Bioorg. Med. Chem. 14, 911–917.

Chai, H., Liang, X.X., Li, L., Zhao, C.S., Gong, P., Liang, Z.J., Zhu, W.L., Jiang, H.L., Luo, C., 2011. Identification of novel 5-hydroxy-1H-indole-3-carboxylates with anti-HBV activities based on 3D QSAR studies. J. Mol. Model. 17, 1831–1840.

Chandran, K., Farsetta, D.L., Nibert, M.L., 2002. Strategy for nonenveloped virus entry: a hydrophobic conformer of the reovirus membrane penetration protein micro 1 mediates membrane disruption. J. Virol. 76, 9920–9933.

Coyne, C.B., Shen, L., Turner, J.R., Bergelson, J.M., 2007. Coxsackievirus entry across epithelial tight junctions requires occludin and the small GTPases Rab34 and Rab5. Cell Host Microbe 2, 181–192.

Delogu, I., Pastorino, B., Baronti, C., Nougairede, A., Bonnet, E., de Lamballerie, X., 2011. In vitro antiviral activity of arbidol against Chikungunya virus and characteristics of a selected resistant mutant. Antiviral Res. 90, 99–107.

Demin, A.V., Martianov, V.A., Shuster, A.M., 2010. Protein kinase C inhibitors exhibiting an anti-inflammatory, anti-allergic and anti-asthma effect. Russian Patent, WO/2010/064958.

Deng, H.Y., Luo, F., Shi, L.Q., Zhong, Q., Liu, Y.J., Yang, Z.Q., 2009. Efficacy of arbidol on lethal hantaan virus infections in suckling mice and in vitro. Acta Pharmacol. Sin. 30, 1015–1024.

Deng, P., Zhong, D., Yu, K., Zhang, Y., Wang, T., Chen, X., 2013. Pharmacokinetics, metabolism, and excretion of the antiviral drug arbidol in humans. Antimicrob. Agents Chemother. 57, 1743–1755.

Drinevskiĭ, V.P., Osidak, L.V., Natsina, V.K., Afanas'eva, O.I., Mil'kint, K.K., Danini, G.V., Ispolatova, A.V., Koreniako, I.E., Karelina, N.N., Marinich, I.G., Boldasov, V.K., 1998. Chemotherapeutics for treatment of influenza and other viral respiratory tract infections in children [Russian]. Antibiot. Khimioter. 43, 29–34.

Eropkin, M.Y., Solovskii, M.V., Smirnova, M.Y., Bryazzhikova, T.S., Gudkova, T.M., Konovalova, N.I., 2009. Synthesis and biological activity of water-soluble polymer complexes of arbidol. Pharm. Chem. J. 43, 563–567.

Fediakina, I.T., Leneva, I.A., Iamnikova, S.S., L'vov, D.K., Glushkov, R.G., Shuster, A.M., 2005. Sensitivity of influenza A/H5 viruses isolated from wild birds on the territory of Russia to arbidol in the cultured MDCK cells [Russian]. Vopr. Virusol. 50, 32–35.

Fediakina, I.T., Shchelkanov, M.I., Deriabin, P.G., Leneva, I.A., Gudova, N.V., Kondrat'eva, T.V., L'vov, D.K., 2011. Susceptibility of pandemic influenza virus A 2009 H1N1 and highly pathogenic avian influenza virus A H5N1 to antiinfluenza agents in cell culture [Russian]. Antibiot. Khimioter. 56, 3–9.

Gagarinova, V.M., Ignat'eva, G.S., Sinitskaia, L.V., Ivanova, A.M., Rodina, M.A., Tur'eva, A.V., 1993. The new chemical preparation arbidol: its prophylactic efficacy during influenza epidemics. Zh. Mikrobiol. Epidemiol. Immunobiol. 5, 40–43 (in Russian).

Gatich, R.Z., Kolobukhina, L.V., Vasil'ev, A.N., Isaeva, E.I., Burtseva, E.I., Orlova, T.G., Voronina, F.V., Kol'tsov, V.D., Malinovskaia, V.V., 2008. Viferon suppositories in the treatment of influenza in adults. Antibiot. Khimioter. 53, 13–17 (Russian).

Glushkov, R.G., 1992. Monograph: arbidol. antiviral, immunostimulant, interferon inducer. Drugs Future 17 (12).

Glushkov, R.G., Gus'kova, T.A., Krylova, L.Iu., Nikolaeva, I.S., 1999. Mechanisms of arbidole's immunomodulating action. Vestn. Ross. Akad. Med. Nauk. 3, 36–40 (Russian).

Gouttenoire, J., Penin, F., Moradpour, D., 2010. Hepatitis C virus nonstructural protein 4B: a journey into unexplored territory. Rev. Med. Virol. 20, 117–129.

Grard, G., Fair, J.N., Lee, D., Slikas, E., et al., 2012. A novel rhabdovirus associated with acute hemorrhagic fever in central Africa. PLoS Pathogens 8 (9), e1002924.

Grimley, P.M., Berezesky, I.K., Friedman, R.M., 1968. Cytoplasmic structures associated with an arbovirus infection: loci of viral ribonucleic acid synthesis. J. Virol. 2, 1326–1338.

Haid, S., Pietschmann, T., Pécheur, E.I., 2009. Low pH-dependent hepatitis C virus membrane fusion depends on E2 integrity, target lipid composition, and density of virus particles. J. Biol. Chem. 284, 17657–17667.

Heaton, N.S., Randall, G., 2011. Dengue virus and autophagy. Viruses 3, 1332–1341. Iatsyshina, S.B., Minenko, A.N., Kushakova, T.E., Praded, M.N., Kudriavtseva, A.V., Shipulin, G.A., Maleev,

V.V., Pokrovskiĭ, V.I., 2010. Pandemic influenza A/H1N1 (sw2009) in Russia: epidemiology, diagnosis, clinical picture, and treatment. Ter. Arkh. 82, 10–14 (Russian).

Inoue, Y., Tanaka, N., Tanaka, Y., Inoue, S., Morita, K., Zhuang, M., Hattori, T., Sugamura, K., 2007. Clathrin-dependent entry of severe acute respiratory syndrome coronavirus into target cells expressing ACE2 with the cytoplasmic tail deleted. J. Virol. 81, 8722–8729.

Johannsdottir, H.K., Mancini, R., Kartenbeck, J., Amato, L., Helenius, A., 2009. Host cell factors and functions involved in vesicular stomatitis virus entry. J. Virol. 83, 440–453.

Khamitov, R.A., Loginova, S.I., Shchukina, V.N., Borisevich, S.V., Maksimov, V.A., Shuster, A.M., 2008. Antiviral activity of arbidol and its derivatives against the pathogen of severe acute respiratory syndrome in the cell cultures. Vopr. Virusol. 53, 9–13 (Russian).

Khan, A.G., Pickl-Herk, A., Gajdzik, L., Marlovits, T.C., Fuchs, R., Blaas, D., 2010. Human rhinovirus 14 enters rhabdomyosarcoma cells expressing ICAM-1 by a clathrin-, caveolin-, and flotillin-independent pathway. J. Virol. 84, 3984–3992.

Kolobukhina, L.V., Malinovskaia, V.V., Gatich, R.Z., Merkulova, L.N., Burtseva, E.I., Isaeva, E.I., Parshina, O.V., Guseva, T.S., Orlova, T.G., Voronina, F.V., 2008. Evaluation of the efficacy of wiferon and arbidol in adult influenza. Vopr. Virusol. 53, 31–33 (Russian).

Kolobukhina, L.V., Merkulova, L.N., Shchelkanov, M.Iu., Burtseva, E.I., Isaeva, E.I., Malyshev, N.A., L'vov, D.K., 2009. Efficacy of ingavirin in adults with influenza. Ter. Arkh. 81, 51–54 (Russian).

Kong, L., Giang, E., Nieusma, T., Kadam, R.U., et al., 2013. Hepatitis C virus E2 envelope glycoprotein core structure. Science 342, 1090–1094.

Krzyzaniak, M.A., Zumstein, M.T., Gerez, J.A., Picotti, P., Helenius, A., 2013. Host cell entry of respiratory syncytial virus involves macropinocytosis followed by proteolytic activation of the F protein. PLoS Pathogens 9, e1003309.

Kujala, P., Ikaheimonen, A., Ehsani, N., Vihinen, H., Auvinen, P., Kaariainen, L., 2001. Biogenesis of the Semliki Forest virus RNA replication complex. J. Virol. 75, 3873–3884.

La Regina, G., Bai, R., Rensen, W.M., et al., 2013. Toward highly potent cancer agents by modulating the C-2 group of the arylthioindole class of tubulin polymerization inhibitors. J. Med. Chem. 56, 123–149.

Leneva, I.A., Sokolova, M.V., Fediakina, I.T., Khristova, M.L., Fadeeva, N.I., Gus'kova, T.A., 2002. Study of the effect of antiviral drugs on the reproduction of the respiratory syncytial virus by enzyme immunoassay. Vopr. Virusol. 47, 42–45 (Russian).

Leneva, I.A., Fediakina, I.T., Gus'kova, T.A., Glushkov, R.G., 2005. Sensitivity of various influenza virus strains to arbidol. Influence of arbidol combination with different antiviral drugs on reproduction of influenza virus A. Ter. Arkh. 77, 84– 88 (Russian).

Leneva, I.A., Shuster, A.M., 2006. Antiviral etiotropic chemicals: efficacy against influenza A viruses A subtype H5N1. Vopr. Virusol. 51, 4–7 (Russian).

Leneva, I.A., Russell, R.J., Boriskin, Y.S., Hay, A.J., 2009. Characteristics of arbidol-resistant mutants of influenza virus: implications for the mechanism of anti-influenza action of arbidol. Antiviral Res. 81, 132–140.

Leneva, I.A., Fediakina, I.T., Eropkin, M.I., Gudova, N.V., Romanovskaia, A.A., Danilenko, D.M., Vinogradova, S.M., Lepeshkin, A.I., Shestopalov, A.M., 2010. Study of the antiviral activity of Russian anti-influenza agents in cell culture and animal models. Vopr. Virusol. 55, 19–27 (Russian).

Leung, J.Y., Ng, M.M., Chu, J.J., 2011. Replication of alphaviruses: a review on the entry process of

alphaviruses into cells. Adv. Virol. 2011, 249640.
Liu, M.Y., Wang, S., Yao, W.F., Wu, H.Z., Meng, S.N., Wei, M.J., 2009. Pharmacokinetic properties and bioequivalence of two formulations of arbidol: an open-label, single-dose, randomized-sequence, two-period crossover study in healthy Chinese male volunteers. Clin. Ther. 31, 784–792.
Liu, Q., Liu, D.Y., Yang, Z.Q., 2013a. Characteristics of human infection with avian influenza viruses and development of new antiviral agents. Acta Pharmacol. Sin. 34, 1257–1269.
Liu, Q., Xiong, H.R., Lu, L., Liu, Y.Y., Luo, F., Hou, W., Yang, Z.Q., 2013b. Antiviral and anti-inflammatory activity of arbidol hydrochloride in influenza A (H1N1) virus infection. Acta Pharmacol. Sin. 34, 1075–1083.
Liu, X., Chen, X.H., Zhang, Y.Y., Liu, W.T., Bi, K.S., 2007a. Determination of arbidol in rat plasma by HPLC–UV using cloud-point extraction. J. Chromatogr. B 856, 273–277.
Liu, X., Huang, Y.W., Li, J., Li, X.B., Bi, K.S., Chen, X.H., 2007b. Determination of arbidol in human plasma by LC–ESI-MS. J. Pharm. Biomed. Anal. 43, 371–375.
Liu, X., Li, H., Bi, K.S., Chen, X.H., Cai, H., Cai, B.C., 2012. Identification of metabolites of arbidol by ultra-high performance liquid chromatography tandem mass spectrometry. Yao Xue Xue Bao 47, 1521–1526 (Chinese).
Liu, X., Huang, T., Chen, J.X., et al., 2013. Arbidol exhibits strong inhibition towards UDP-glucuronosyltransferase (UGT) 1A9 and 2B7. Pharmazie 68, 945–950.
Loginova, S.I., Borisevich, S.V., Maksimov, V.A., Bondarev, V.P., Nebol'sin, V.E., 2008. Therapeutic efficacy of Ingavirin, a new domestic formulation against influenza A virus (H3N2). Antibiot. Khimioter. 53, 27–30 (Russian).
Loginova, S.I., Borisevich, S.V., Maksimov, V.A., Bondarev, V.P., 2009. Toxicity estimation of unspecific medicinal antiviral agents for prophylaxis and therapy of hazard and especially hazard viral infections. Antibiot. Khimioter. 54, 11–14 (Russian).
Lozach, P.Y., Mancini, R., Bitto, D., Meier, R., Oestereich, L., Överby, A., Pettersson, R., Helenius, A., 2010. Entry of bunyaviruses into mammalian cells. Cell Host Microbe 7, 488–499.
L'vov, D.K., Burtseva, E.I., Kolobukhina, L.V., Feodoritova, E.L., Shevchenko, E.S., et al., 2013. Development of the influenza epidemic in season 2011–2012 in some areas of Russia: results of activity of the influenza etiology and epidemiology center of the ivanovsky institute of virology. Vopr. Virusol. 58, 15–20 (Russian).
Martinez, C.G., Guinea, R., Benavente, J., Carrasco, L., 1996. The entry of reovirus into L cells is dependent on vacuolar proton-ATPase activity. J. Virol. 70, 576–579.
Mercer, J., Helenius, A., 2009. Virus entry by macropinocytosis. Nat. Cell Biol. 11, 510–520.
Meertens, L., Bertaux, C., Dragic, T., 2006. Hepatitis C virus entry requires a critical postinternalization step and delivery to early endosomes via clathrin-coated vesicles. J. Virol. 80, 11571–11578.
Metz, R., Muth, P., Ferger, M., Kukes, V.G., Vergin, H., 1998. Sensitive high-performance liquid chromatographic determination of arbidol, a new antiviral compound, in human plasma. J. Chromatogr. A 810, 63–69.
Miller, L., Bergeron, R., 1994. Preparative liquid chromatographic isolation of unknown impurities in Arbidol and SI-5. J. Chromatogr. A 658, 489–496.
Moradpour, D., Penin, F., Rice, C.M., 2007. Replication of Hepatitis C virus. Nature Rev. Microbiol. 5, 453–463.
Nasser, Z.H., Swaminathan, K., Muller, P., Downard, K.M., 2013. Inhibition of influenza hemagglutinin with the antiviral inhibitor arbidol using a proteomics based approach and mass

spectrometry. Antiviral Res. 100, 399–406.
Obrosova-Serova, N.P., Burtseva, E.I., Nevskiı˘, I.M., Karmanova, R.I., Nazarov, V.I., Pitkenen, A.A., Slepushkin, A.N., 1991. The protective action of arbidol during a rise in respiratory diseases in 1990. Vopr. Virusol. 36, 380–381 (Russian).
Pécheur, E.I., Lavillette, D., Alcaras, F., Molle, J., Boriskin, Y.S., Roberts, M., Cosset, F.L., Polyak, S.J., 2007. Biochemical mechanism of hepatitis C virus inhibition by the broad-spectrum antiviral arbidol. Biochemistry 46, 6050–6059.
Romanovskaia, A.A., Durymanov, A.M., Sharshov, K.A., et al., 2009. Investigation of susceptibility of influenza viruses A (H1N1), the cause of infection in humans in April–May 2009, to antivirals in MDCK cell culture. Antibiot. Khimioter. 54, 41– 47 (Russian).
Romero-Brey, I., Merz, A., Chiramel, A., Lee, J.Y., Chlanda, P., Haselman, U., Santarella-Mellwig, R., Habermann, A., Hoppe, S., Kallis, S., Walther, P., Antony, C., Krijnse-Locker, J., Bartenschlager, R., 2012. Three-dimensional architecture and biogenesis of membrane structures associated with hepatitis C virus replication. PLoS Pathogens 8, e1003056.
Sellitto, G., Faruolo, A., de Caprariis, P., Altamura, S., Paonessa, G., Ciliberto, G., 2010. Synthesis and anti-hepatitis C virus activity of novel ethyl 1H-indole-3-carboxylates in vitro. Bioorg. Med. Chem. 18, 6143–6148.
Semenenko, T.A., Sel'kova, E.P., Gotvianskaia, T.P., Gaı˘darenko, A.D., Polezhaeva, N.A., Evseeva, L.F., Nikolaeva, O.G., 2005. Characteristics of the immune status in specific and nonspecific prophylaxis of influenza in elderly persons. Zh. Mikrobiol. Epidemiol. Immunobiol. 6, 24–28 (Russian).
Shi, L., Xiong, H., He, J., Deng, H., Li, Q., Zhong, Q., Hou, W., Cheng, L., Xiao, H., Yang, Z., 2007. Antiviral activity of arbidol against influenza A virus, respiratory syncytial virus, rhinovirus, coxsackie virus and adenovirus in vitro and in vivo. Arch. Virol. 152, 1447–1455.
Shumilov, V.I., Shuster, A.M., Lobastov, S.P., Shevtsov, V.A., Mednikov, B.L., Piiavskiı˘, S.A., Litus, V.I., 2002. Efficacy of arbidol in prophylaxis and treatment of acute respiratory viral infections in servicemen. Voen. Med. Zh. 323 (51–3), 96 (Russian).
Shuster, A.M., Shumilov, V.I., Shevtsov, V.A., Mar'in, G.G., Kozlov, V.N., 2004. Arbidol used in the prophylaxis of acute respiratory viral infections and their complications in servicemen. Voen. Med. Zh. 325 (44–5), 80 (Russian).
Solignat, M., Gay, B., Higgs, S., Briant, L., Devaux, C., 2009. Replication cycle of chikungunya: a re-emerging arbovirus. Virology 393, 183–197.
Song, J.H., Fang, Z.Z., Zhu, L.L., Cao, Y.F., Hu, C.M., Ge, G.B., Zhao, D.W., 2013. Glucuronidation of the broad-spectrum antiviral drug arbidol by UGT isoforms. J. Pharm. Pharmacol. 65, 521–527.
Sun, Y., He, X., Qiu, F., Zhu, X., Zhao, M., Li-Ling, J., Su, X., Zhao, L., 2013. Pharmacokinetics of single and multiple oral doses of arbidol in healthy Chinese volunteers. Int. J. Clin. Pharmacol. Ther. 51, 423–432.
Teissier, E., Penin, F., Pécheur, E.I., 2010. Targeting cell entry of enveloped viruses as an antiviral strategy. Molecules 16, 221–250.
Teissier, E., Zandomeneghi, G., Loquet, A., Lavillette, D., Lavergne, J.P., Montserret, R., Cosset, F.L., Bockmann, A., Meier, B.H., Penin, F., Pécheur, E.I., 2011. Mechanism of inhibition of enveloped virus membrane fusion by the antiviral drug arbidol. PLoS ONE 6, e15874.
Trofimov, F.A., Tsyshkova, N.G., Zotova, S.A., Grinev, A.N., 1993. Synthesis of a new antiviral agent, arbidole. Pharm. Chem. J. 27, 75–76.
von Kleist, L., Stahlschmidt, W., Bulut, H., et al., 2011. Role of the clathrin terminal domain in

regulating coated pit dynamics revealed by small molecule inhibition. Cell 146, 471–484.

Wang, M.Z., Cai, B.Q., Li, L.Y., Lin, J.T., Su, N., Yu, H.X., Gao, H., Zhao, J.Z., Liu, L., 2004. Efficacy and safety of arbidol in treatment of naturally acquired influenza. Zhongguo Yi Xue Ke Xue Yuan Xue Bao 26, 289–293 (Chinese).

Wang, M., Shu, B., Bai, W.X., Liu, J., Yao, J., Pan, W.N., Pan, Y.Y., 2010. A 4-week oral toxicity study of an antiviral drug combination consisting of arbidol and acetaminophen in rats. Drug Chem. Toxicol. 33, 244–253.

Wang, Y., Chen, X., Li, Q., Zhong, D., 2008. Metabolite identification of arbidol in human urine by the study of CID fragmentation pathways using HPLC coupled with ion trap mass spectrometry. J. Mass Spectrom. 43, 1099–1109.

Wei, F., Li, J.L., Ling, J.X., et al., 2013. Establishment of SYBR green-based qPCR assay for rapid evaluation and quantification for anti-Hantaan virus compounds in vitro and in suckling mice. Virus Genes 46, 54–62.

Yan, H., Zhong, G., Xu, G., He, W., Jing, Z., et al., 2012. Sodium taurocholate cotransporting polypeptide is a functional receptor for human hepatitis B and D virus. Elife 1, e00049.

Zhao, C., Zhao, Y., Chai, H., Gong, P., 2006. Synthesis and in vitro anti-hepatitis B virus activities of some ethyl 5-hydroxy-1H-indole-3-carboxylates. Bioorg. Med. Chem. 14, 2552–2558.

Zhong, Q., Yang, Z., Liu, Y., Deng, H., Xiao, H., Shi, L., He, J., 2009. Antiviral activity of Arbidol against Coxsackie virus B5 in vitro and in vivo. Arch. Virol. 154, 601–607.

Biochemical Mechanism of Hepatitis C Virus Inhibition by the Broad-Spectrum Antiviral Arbidol

Eve-Isabelle Pécheur,[*,3] Dimitri Lavillette,[§] Fanny Alcaras,[3] Jennifer Molle,[3] Yury S. Boriskin,[μ] Michael Roberts,[@] François-Loïc Cosset,[§] and Stephen J. Polyak[#]

IFR128 Biosciences Lyon Gerland, Institut de Biologie et Chimie des Protéines, UMR 5086 CNRS-Université Claude Bernard Lyon I, 7 passage du Vercors, 69367 Lyon Cedex 07, France, Université de Lyon (UCBL 1), IFR128 Biosciences Lyon Gerland, INSERM, U758, Lyon, and Ecole Normale Supérieure de Lyon, F-69007 Lyon, France, Institute of Virology, Medical Academy of Sciences, Moscow, Russia, Global Phasing Ltd., Sheraton House, Castle Park, Cambridge CB3 0AX, U.K., and Virology Division, Department of Laboratory Medicine, School of Medicine, University of Washington, 325 9th Avenue, Seattle, Washington 98104-2499

Received January 29, 2007; Revised Manuscript Received March 22, 2007

ABSTRACT: Hepatitis C affects 3% of the world population, yet its current treatment options are limited to interferon-ribavirin drug regimens which achieve a 50-70% cure rate depending on the hepatitis C virus (HCV) genotype. Besides extensive screening for HCV-specific compounds, some well-established medicinal drugs have recently demonstrated an anti-HCV effect in HCV replicon cells. One of these drugs is arbidol (ARB), a Russian-made broad-spectrum antiviral agent, which we have previously shown to inhibit acute and chronic HCV infection. Here we show that ARB inhibits the cell entry of HCV pseudoparticles of genotypes 1a, 1b, and 2a in a dose-dependent fashion. ARB also displayed a dose-dependent inhibition of HCV membrane fusion, as assayed by using HCV pseudoparticles (HCVpp) and fluorescent liposomes. ARB inhibition of HCVpp fusion was found to be more effective on genotype 1a than on genotypes 1b and 2a. In vitro biochemical studies revealed association of ARB with membranelike environments such as detergents and with lipid membranes. This association was particularly prominent at acidic pH which is optimal for HCV-mediated fusion. Our results suggest that the affinity of ARB for lipid membranes could account for its anti-HCV actions, together with a differential level of interaction with key motifs in HCV glycoproteins of different genotypes.

The hepatitis C virus (HCV)[1] infects an estimated 3% or 170 million of the world's population, and hepatitis C is now the most frequent indication for liver transplantation. Current treatment options are limited to pegylated recombinant interferon R (IFN-R) in combination with ribavirin. However, viremia eradication is variably achieved depending on the genotype, with only 50% of virus eradication in genotype-1 infected patients.

[ž]This work was supported by the ANRS (Agence Nationale de Recherches sur le SIDA et les hépatites virales) (E.-I.P.), by the French CNRS and INSERM, by LSHB-CT-2004-005246 (COMPUVAC) to F.-L.C., and by the Ligue Nationale Contre le Cancer and the Rhône-Alpes Region. Y.S.B. was partially supported by the Fulbright Visiting Scholar Program. S.J.P. is supported by NIH Grants RO1 DK62187 and U19 A1066328.

* To whom correspondence should be addressed: IBCP, UMR 5086 CNRS-UCBL, 7 passage du Vercors, 69367 Lyon Cedex 07, France. Phone: 33-4-72-72-26-44. Fax: 33-4-72-72-26-04. E-mail: e.pecheur@ ibcp.fr.

[3] UMR 5086 CNRS-Université Claude Bernard Lyon I.

[§] Université de Lyon, INSERM, and Ecole Normale Supérieure de Lyon.

[|] These authors contributed equally to this work. [μ] Medical Academy of Sciences.

[@] Global Phasing Ltd.

[#] University of Washington.

[1] Abbreviations: ARB, arbidol; chol, cholesterol; cmc, critical micellar concentration; DM, dodecyl maltoside; HA, influenza hemag-glutinin; HCV, hepatitis C virus; HCVpp, HCV pseudoparticles; PC, phosphatidylcholine; alpha-lysoPC, L-alpha-palmitoyllysophosphatidylcholine; PS, phosphatidylserine; R_{18}, octadecyl rhodamine B chloride; RD114, feline endogenous oncoretrovirus RD114; SDS, sodium dodecyl sulfate.

This is clearly a problem in North America, Europe, and Japan, where genotype 1 is the most prevalent genotype. HCV therefore appears to be resistant to IFN antiviral therapy, and this is likely to be due to some factors of viral origin (*1*).

Historically, the development of new anti-HCV drugs has been hampered due to the lack of cell culture and small animal models that are required for preclinical evaluations of antiviral compounds. The generation of an HCV replicon system (*2*) has afforded massive antiviral drug screening efforts (*3*). Distinct from specific anti-HCV compounds that target key viral functions are a group of broad-spectrum medicinal drugs that were originally designed for other treatments or targeted toward other viruses. Using the replicon system, these compounds have been shown to possess potent antiviral activity toward HCV (*4*, *5*). The advantage of this group of antivirals is that they have already met the pharmacological criteria for medicinal drugs and are already approved for clinical use in some countries.

One of these compounds, the Russian-made arbidol µ ARB; 1*H*-indole-3-carboxylic acid, 6-bromo-4-[(dimethylamino)-methyl]-5-hydroxy-1-methyl-2-[(phenylthio)methyl]-, ethyl ester, monohydrochloride; CAS Registry Number 131707-23-8 (Figure 1)µ , was originally described as an anti-influenza drug with purported immunostimulant properties (*6*). ARB has been licensed for several years in Russia for

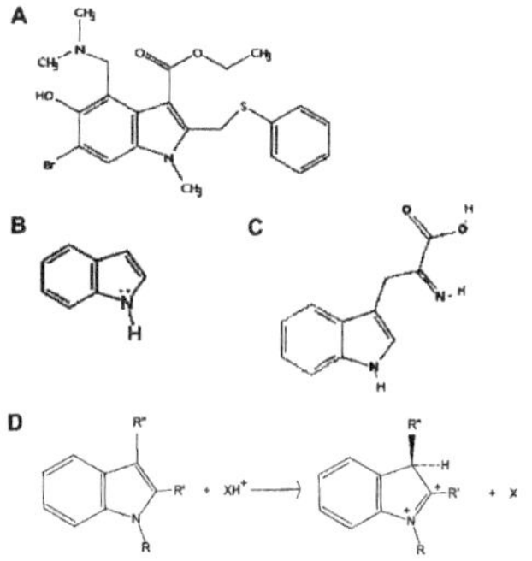

FIGURE 1: Structures of arbidol (A), indole (B), and tryptophan (C). (D) Scheme of the protonation of substituted indole and its effect on the 3-position (from ref 22).

use as prophylaxis and treatment for influenza A and B infections. It allegedly exerts its effect by activation of macrophage phagocytic activity and may also stimulate aspects of cellular and humoral immunity. ARB inhibits influenza virus-induced membrane fusion and may have the capacity to induce serum interferon (*7*). More recent studies extended its inhibitory activity to other human viruses such as the respiratory syncytial virus, parainfluenza virus 3, rhinovirus 14 (*8*), and hepatitis B virus (*9*). Bird viruses such as the avian coronavirus and the H5/N1 influenza A virus were shown to be sensitive to ARB as well (*10*, *11*). We recently demonstrated that ARB inhibits both acute and chronic HCV infection in vitro and HCV replication using the HCV replicon system (*12*). In the study presented here, we further characterize ARB's mechanism of action. We present a detailed biochemical characterization of interactions of ARB with membranes and examine how ARB can inhibit HCV entry by using HCV pseudoparticles (HCVpp). We found that ARB inhibited the infection of cells with HCVpp of different genotypes, through the inhibition of HCVpp-mediated membrane fusion. This inhibition was particularly prominent at acidic pH that is optimal for association of ARB with membranes.

EXPERIMENTAL PROCEDURES

Chemicals. Sodium dodecyl sulfate (SDS), *n*-dodecyl *beta*-D-maltoside (DM), L-alpha-palmitoyllysophosphatidylcholine (alpha-lysoPC), phosphatidylcholine from egg yolk (PC, 99% pure), cholesterol (chol, 99% pure), and Triton X-100 were purchased from Sigma. Phosphatidylserine (PS) from porcine brain was from Avanti Polar Lipids (Alabaster, AL). Octadecyl rhodamine B chloride (R_{18}) was from Molecular Probes. Arbidol μ ARB, 1*H*-indole-3-carboxylic acid, 6-bromo-4-[(dimethylamino)methyl]-5-hydroxy-1-methyl-2-[(phenylthio)methyl]-, ethyl ester, monohydrochloride (Figure 1A)μ was a kind gift from A. M. Schuster and I. A. Leneva. ARB was first dissolved in absolute ethanol and then taken to the final concentration (100 mM) in sterile twice-distilled water. The final concentration of ethanol in contact with membranes varied between 0.011 and 1.1%o.

Vector Constructs, Preparation of Pseudoparticles, and Infection Assay. The CMV-Gag-Pol murine leukemia virus (MLV) packaging construct, encoding the MLV *gag* and *pol* genes, and the MLV-GFP plasmid, encoding a MLV-based transfer vector containing a CMV-GFP internal transcrip-tional unit, were described previously (*13*). The phCMV-HA (*14*) and NA expression vectors encode the hemagglu-tinin and neuraminidase of fowl plague virus, respectively. phCMV-E1E2-HCV (*13*) encodes both HCV E1 and E2 glycoproteins of genotype 1a, strain H77 (AF009606), of genotype 1b (AY734975 clone UKN1b12.6 and AF333324), or of genotype 2a, isolate JFH-1 (AB047639). The phCMV-RD expression vector encodes the feline endogenous on-coretrovirus RD114 glycoprotein (*15*).

Pseudoparticles bearing either the E1 and E2 envelope glycoproteins of HCV (HCVpp), the hemagglutinin of the influenza virus (HApp), or the RD114 envelope protein (RD114) were then generated and purified as previously described (*13, 16*). Infection of Huh7 cells with concentrated pseudoparticles was performed in the absence or presence of increasing concentrations of ARB (between 0.1 and 6 μg/ mL), added to the cell culture medium as the ethanol/water stock solution. ARB was added to cells at increasing concentrations but under similar volumes, either before or after pseudoparticle binding. After that step, cell culture medium was removed and replaced with fresh medium, and infection was assessed 72 h later by FACS analysis. Values obtained with HCVpp on untreated cells were taken to be 100%.

Fluorescence Assays. PC/chol (70:30 molar ratio) or PS large unilamellar vesicles (100 nm) were prepared as described previously (*16*). R_{18}-labeled PS liposomes were added to unlabeled PS vesicles in PBS, in a 4:1 unlabeled: labeled ratio. After a 2 min equilibration at 37 μ C, $CaCl_2$ was added to a final Ca^{2+} concentration of 2 mM to initiate membrane fusion. A similar experiment was performed in the presence of arbidol.

The spectral properties of ARB were investigated by spectrophotometry and spectrofluorimetry, in phosphate-buffered saline (PBS) at pH 7.4, in the absence or presence of detergent micelles or liposomes. Spectral properties of indole derivatives such as tryptophan or ARB (see Figure 1) depend on their microenvironment, which in turn influ-ences the maximum position (λ_{max}) and quantum yield of their fluorescence. Fluorescence was recorded on an SLM Aminco 8000 fluorimeter, with excitation slits set to 8 nm and emission slits to 4 nm. The excitation polarizer was oriented at 90µ relative to the vertical, and 0µ for emission, to improve the spectral resolution of the fluorescence and minimize scattering effects (*17*). Spectra were measured using a 10 mm x 2 mm quartz cuvette. Emission spectra were collected in the 300-450 nm region with an increment of 1 nm and corrected for vesicle light scattering (*17, 18*). The increase in quantum yield is given by F/F_0, where F and F_0 denote the fluorescence at 340 nm after and before addition of detergent or liposomes, respectively. The measure of fusion between pseudoparticles and liposomes was based upon a lipid mixing assay, as described in details elsewhere (*16*). ARB was preincubated for 2 min with either pseudoparticles or liposomes, before lipid mixing was initiated by decreasing the pH to 5.0.

RESULTS

Arbidol Blocks Cell Infection by HCVpp. We sought to determine whether ARB had any effect on HCV entry,

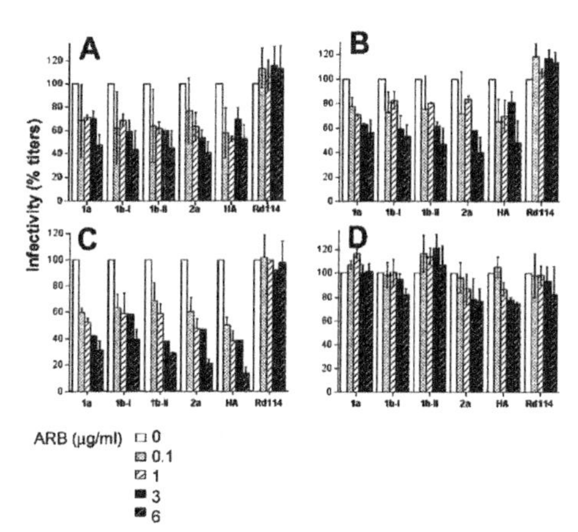

FIGURE 2: Effect of arbidol on HCVpp infectivity. Huh-7 cells were seeded at 4x10[4] cells per well in 24-well plates the day before infection (day -1). At day 0, HCVpp (as a 100x concentrated fraction; see Experimental Procedures) were added to cells and incubated for 3 h at 37µ C, in the absence or presence of arbidol (see Experimental Procedures for other details). (A) ARB was added at indicated concentrations during the course of infection. (B) ARB was first preincubated at indicated concentrations with concentrated pseudoparticles for 3 h, and infection was then performed in the presence of the same concentration of ARB. (C and D) ARB was preincubated at indicated concentrations with Huh-7 cells for 3 h before infection, and HCVpp infection was performed in the presence (C) or absence (D) of ARB. HCV pseudoparticles that were tested were harboring the E1 and E2 glycoproteins of genotypes 1a (AF009606), 1b (AY734975 for 1b-I and AF333324 for 1b-II), and 2a (AB047639). HApp and RD114pp are shown as positive and negative controls, respectively. Infectivity is expressed as the percentage of control, i.e., pseudoparticle infection of Huh-7 cells not treated with ARB, taken to be 100%. Results are the mean (standard deviation of four separate experiments.

namely, whether ARB could affect the infection of cultured cells by HCVpp. The results of these experiments are presented in Figure 2, where HApp and RD114pp were used as controls. When ARB was present during the course of HCVpp infection (Figure 2A), a decrease in infectivity was observed for all HCV genotypes tested, and the inhibition effect was proportional to ARB concentration. The maximal reduction (50% inhibition) in infectivity was observed at 6 μg/mL ARB (11.3 μM). When HCVpp were preincubated with ARB before infection, with subsequent continuous ARB present during infection, a dose-dependent inhibition of infection was again observed for all genotypes that were tested (Figure 2B), with a maximum of 50% inhibition at 6 μg/mL ARB. The most pronounced inhibition was seen when Huh-7 cells were preincubated with ARB for 3 h and then left in the presence of ARB onward. Under these conditions (Figure 2C), the 50% inhibition was achieved at 1 μg/mL ARB (1.88 μM). Infectivity was further reduced at 6 íg/mL ARB, with up to 70% inhibition for genotypes 1a and 1b and even 80% for genotype 2a. The HApp behaved in a very similar way, showing a dose-dependent decrease in their infectivity (Figure 2A-C), with a maximal ARB effect at 6 μg/mL (from 40 to 90% inhibition). Note that a drastic reduction in infectivity (90% inhibition) could also be observed when cells were preincubated overnight with ARB, with no toxicity observed (data not shown). Conversely, cell infection by RD114pp was unaffected by the presence of ARB, whatever drug concentration was tested and whatever infection conditions were designed. This suggests that ARB might achieve a certain level of specificity toward some viral glycoproteins, in particular, HCV and influenza glycoproteins in our study.

Interestingly, when cells were preincubated with ARB for 3 h, but the drug was removed from cells immediately before HCVpp infection, no significant effect on HCVpp infectivity was observed (Figure 2D), although we noted an up to 20% reduction in infectivity of HCVpp-2a and HApp at the highest concentrations of ARB (6 μg/mL).

Taken together, these data indicate that ARB exerts its inhibitory effect on infection when it is in physical contact with either the pseudoparticles, cell membranes, or both, and prominently at acidic pH. The absence of infection inhibition observed after withdrawal of ARB from the incubation medium before infection suggests that its transient accumula-tion at the cell surface and/or in intracellular compartments is not enough to exert sustained HCV inhibitory action. The effect of ARB on HCVpp-mediated fusion and the role of pH were next directly tested in our in vitro lipid mixing assay (*16*).

Arbidol Inhibits HCVpp-Mediated Lipid Mixing. The effect of arbidol on HCVpp membrane fusion activity is presented in Figure 3. After the pH was decreased to 5.0, a rapid and significant dequenching was observed as a measure of lipid mixing between HCVpp and R_{18}-labeled liposomes, for genotypes 1a (Figure 3A; see also ref *16*), 1b (Figure 3B), and 2a (Figure 3C). In the presence of ARB, HCVpp fusion ability was inhibited. This inhibition was directly proportional to ARB concentration, with some variations among HCV genotypes, though. Indeed, the most prominent inhibition of fusion by ARB was observed for genotype 1a, where fusion was completely abolished at 1 μg/mL ARB (1.88 μM). Conversely, a similar block in fusion was achieved at only 6 μg/mL ARB (11.3 μM) for genotype 1b. For genotype 2a, a measurable fusion was still observed at this concentration. This observation was reproducible ($n = 4$), but the reason for that difference in fusion behavior between genotypes is at present unclear. ARB concentrations higher than 6 μg/ mL were not tested to avoid toxicity to the cells (*12*). Note also that immunoblot analyses of the glycoproteins revealed that they were present in each viral preparation (data not shown and ref *16*). We also controlled the global input of the different pseudoparticles by estimating the amount of

MLV core protein in each viral preparation on immunoblots. This amount of core was similar for all pseudoparticle preparations assayed in fusion (data not shown and ref *16*). We suggest that ARB might differentially interact with HCV glycoproteins of different genotypes (see Discussion). Note that the fusion mediated by RD114pp could not be investi-gated in our assay, since the RD114 glycoprotein is activated for fusion in a pH-independent but receptor-dependent manner (data not shown).

The inhibition of fusion by ARB was comparable when ARB was preincubated with HCVpp or with liposomes (data not shown). ARB-induced inhibition is also not dependent upon the lipid composition of liposomes, since similar HCV fusion inhibition was observed with plain PC (not shown) or with PC/chol liposomes (Figure 3).

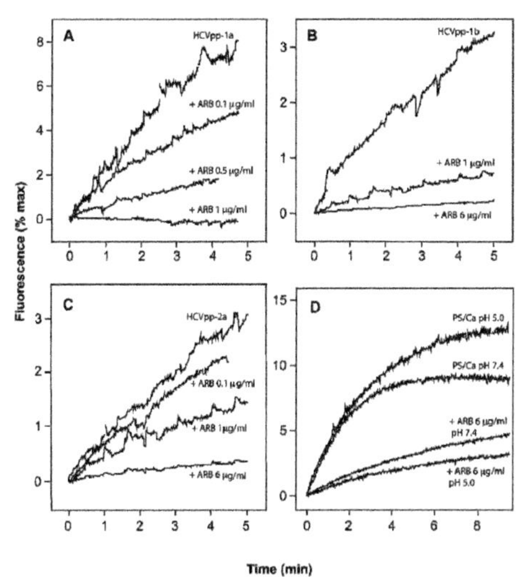

FIGURE 3: Arbidol inhibits HCVpp-mediated lipid mixing. Lipid mixing curves of HCVpp genotypes 1a (A), 1b (B), and 2a (C), in the absence or presence of ARB, with R_{18}-labeled liposomes (representative of four separate experiments). Pseudoparticles (40 ίL) were added to R_{18}-labeled PC/chol liposomes (final lipid concentration of 15 μM), in PBS (pH 7.4) at 37μ C, with or without indicated concentrations of ARB. After a 2 min equilibration, lipid mixing was initiated by decreasing the pH to 5.0 (time 0), and the spectrum was recorded as R_{18} fluorescence dequenching as a function of time. (D) Influence of ARB on Ca^{2+}-induced fusion of PS vesicles. Liposomes consisting of PS and R_{18} (96:4) were mixed with nonlabeled PS vesicles (1:4 molar ratio) in 5 mM Hepes and 100 mM NaCl (pH 7.4) at 37 μ C, at a final lipid concentration of 100 μM. Fusion was induced by rapid injection of Ca^{2+} into the medium (final concentration of 2 mM), and the kinetics of lipid dilution was continuously monitored. ARB was incubated with labeled and nonlabeled PS vesicles for 1 min in buffer at pH 7.4 or 5.0 (by adding diluted HCl), and then Ca^{2+} was added at a final concentration of 2 mM to initiate fusion.

We next asked whether ARB could inhibit fusion in other membrane systems as well. We therefore investigated the effect of ARB on the Ca-induced fusion of PS liposomes (*19*). Kinetics of PS vesicle lipid mixing by Ca^{2+} were comparable at neutral and acidic pH (Figure 3D), as previously reported (*20*). In the presence of 6 ίg/mL ARB, inhibition of lipid mixing was observed at both pH's, but with a more pronounced effect at acidic than neutral pH (Figure 3D). The spectral properties of ARB were not affected by Ca^{2+} (data not shown), which rules out the direct interaction between ARB and Ca^{2+} that would artifactually lead to fusion inhibition.

Altogether, these results suggest that ARB is a membrane fusion inhibitor, exerting its effect on viral (protein-induced) fusion and on a protein-free membrane fusion systems. Thus, ARB might associate with membranes to exert its inhibitory effect. However, this is probably not its only mode of action, since (i) HCVpp of different genotypes have differential sensitivity to the antiviral effects of ARB and (ii) in contrast to HA and HCV E1/E2, RD114 envelope protein is not sensitive to ARB. These observations suggest that ARB might differentially interact with key motifs in HCV fusion protein(s), sequences that might differ among HCV geno-types. Moreover, ARB acts predominantly at low pH. In our in vitro fusion assays, two hypotheses might explain such a behavior: ARB could block fusion either by counteracting the acidification process like chloroquine (*21*) and/or through its protonated form at low pH [see Figure 1D for the protonated form of a substituted indole (*22*)]. Since the Ca-induced PS liposome fusion system is not pH-dependent but is markedly inhibited by ARB at low pH, the first hypothesis of ARB blocking endosomal acidification as an explanation for ARB-induced fusion inhibition was deemed unlikely. Nonetheless, since ARB is a weak base (Figure 1), we tested this hypothesis directly. To this end, increasing concentra-tions of ARB (1, 10, and 50 μg/mL) were added to the suspension of HCVpp and liposomes in PBS (pH 7.4). After a 2 min equilibration, an exactly measured volume of diluted HCl required to decrease the pH to 5.0 was added in each tube, and the pH was recorded with the pH meter. Within the tested range of ARB concentrations from 1 to 50 μg/ mL, we could detect only slight pH variations of no more than 0.1 pH unit (data not shown). Such a narrow pH range alteration could be critical for influenza virus-induced fusion (HApp) but is unlikely to affect the broad-spectrum (pH 5.0-6.3) fusogenic properties of HCV (*16*, *23*, *24*). Therefore, our results essentially ruled out the direct buffering role of ARB as an explanation for its fusion inhibition. The behavior of ARB at low pH will be examined in detail in the next paragraphs.

Spectral Properties of Arbidol in Solution. ARB is an indole derivative and shares this structure with tryptophan (Trp) (Figure 1). The preference of indole derivatives for membrane interfaces (and specifically of Trp in membrane proteins) is now well-documented (*25*, *26*). This interfacial preference is related to the flat rigid structure of these molecules and to their aromaticity which allows them to establish cation-∂ interactions with lipid headgroups, i.e., interactions between the indole ring through its π-electron cloud and the nitrogen of the lipid headgroup (*25*, *27*). We therefore reasoned that ARB might behave in a similar way, i.e., that it might enter into similar interactions between its indole group (Figure 1B) and the $N(CH_3)_3^+$ group of phosphatidylcholine. To investigate behavior of ARB toward membranes, we first analyzed its spectral properties in solution. Its light absorption properties were studied by spectrophotometry over a 240-700 nm wavelength range. The ARB absorbance peaked at 255 nm (λ_{exc}) and 315 nm, both at pH 7.4 (Figure 4, dotted line) and at pH 5.0 (data not shown). The former λ_{exc} was then used as the excitation wavelength to study ARB fluorescence properties, since we reasoned that a shorter excitation wavelength would improve spectral separation of emission and scattering (see also ref *17*). To achieve an adequate signal-to-noise ratio, we have analyzed the average of five emission spectra (Figure 4, solid lines). In PBS at pH 7.4, ARB displays a λ_{max} at 360 nm (thin solid line); this λ_{max} is slightly blue shifted to 357 nm at pH 5.0 (thick solid line). For our further investigations of ARB behavior toward membranes or membranelike environments, a λ_{exc} of 255 nm and a λ_{em} of 350 nm were then used, unless otherwise indicated.

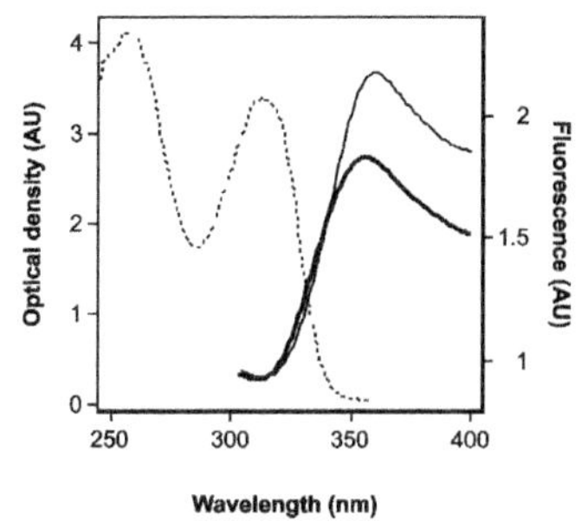

FIGURE 4: Fluorescence properties of arbidol. All measurements were recorded at 37 μ C, with excitation (exc) and emission (em) slits set to 8 and 4 nm, respectively. Relative orientations of exc and em polarizers were 90μ and 0μ, respectively. ARB absorbance (dotted line) was recorded at pH 7.4, and fluorescence emission spectra were recorded at pH 7.4 (thin solid line) or pH 5.0 (thick solid line). Fluorescence was monitored using a 113 μM (60 μg/ mL) ARB solution, with a λ_{exc} of 255 nm.

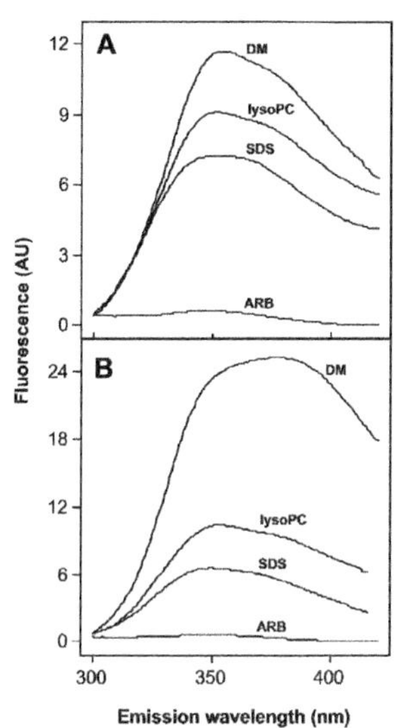

FIGURE 5: Interaction of arbidol with detergent micelles. Fluorescence conditions were similar to those in Figure 4. ARB (18.8 μM, 10 μg/mL) was added to PBS buffer containing either 100 mM SDS, 100 μM α-lysoPC, 100 mM DM, or no detergent (A) at pH 7.4 or (B) pH 5.0.

Arbidol Interacts with Detergent Micelles. Three detergents were chosen as membranelike environments to study the interaction of ARB with micelles: sodium dodecyl sulfate (SDS, negatively charged), dodecyl maltoside (DM, neutral and of a glucidic nature), and α-palmitoyllysophosphatidyl-choline (zwitterionic and of a lipidic nature). At detergent concentrations well above the critical micellar concentration [cmc (*28*)], and at pH 7.4, the addition of ARB to micelles led to a dramatic increase in the quantum yield of fluores-cence for each detergent that was tested (Figure 5A and Table 1), in the following order: DM > α-lysoPC > SDS.

Table 1: Fluorescence Characteristics of Arbidol in Buffer, in the Presence of Detergent Micelles, or in the Presence of PC/chol Liposomes[a]

medium	λ_{max} (nm)	F/F_0 (340 nm)[b]
PBS at pH 7.4	360	-
PBS at pH 5.0	357	-
pH 7.4		
100 mM SDS	351	11.88
100 íM R-lysoPC	352	14.14
100 mM DM	354	16.99
12.5 μM PC/chol	351	0.99
25.0 μM PC/chol	344	1.18
62.5 μM PC/chol	342	1.36
100 μM PC/chol	338	1.54
pH 5.0		
100 mM SDS	348	6.42
100 μM R-lysoPC	350	9.38
100 mM DM	377	20.58
12.5 μM PC/chol	353	1.28
25.0 μM PC/chol	345	1.41
62.5 μM PC/chol	338	1.81

[a] All measurements were performed at 37µ C after a 5 min pre-equilibration. [b] Variation in the fluorescence quantum yield is expressed as F/F_0, where F and F_0 denote the fluorescence intensity at 340 nm after and before addition of detergent or PC/chol liposomes, respectively.

This effect was even more pronounced at pH 5.0, where the increase in quantum yield was concomitant to a moderate blue shift of the maximum emission wavelength for SDS and R-lysoPC (Figure 5B and Table 1). These two phenomena are indicative of an association of ARB with micelles, accompanied by a partial, and most likely, superficial burial of the ARB molecule into the micelles. This interaction is more pronounced at acidic pH, where the ARB molecule is more protonated than at neutral pH. This suggests that the protonated form of ARB is probably more effective at inhibiting membrane fusion than the actual ARB molecule.

We then monitored the binding of ARB at pH 5.0 to increasing concentrations of SDS, α-lysoPC, and DM micelles from the resulting fluorescence changes at 350 nm (Figure 5). Results are shown in Figure 6. The shapes of the three binding curves are similar, showing that binding was similar in all cases. For all detergents that were studied, a steep increase in fluorescence was observed till the cmc value of the detergent was reached (*28*). From detergent concentrations above the cmc, fluorescence plateaued, which indicates that virtually all ARB molecules are bound to micelles at high detergent concentrations. Under these conditions, almost all of the observed ARB fluorescence was therefore due to ARB incorporated into or interacting with the detergent micelles. This confirms the affinity and tropism of ARB for membranelike environments, particularly at acidic pH.

The influence of pH on binding of ARB to detergent micelles was then studied using DM solely, since this detergent gave rise to the largest increase in fluorescence quantum yield (Figure 5 and Table 1) and is neutral. When ARB was added to a 5 mM solution of DM in a buffer, it appeared clearly that ARB fluorescence increased while pH was decreasing (Figure 7A). The increase in ARB fluores-cence between pH 7.4 and 4.5 at 350 nm is 60%, as shown in Figure 7B. Since we know from the previous experiment that for the ARB:DM ratio used here (1:266), virtually all ARB molecules are bound to micelles, the observed fluo-rescence increase with a pH decrease may arise from a difference in ARB ionization state at neutral or acidic pH.

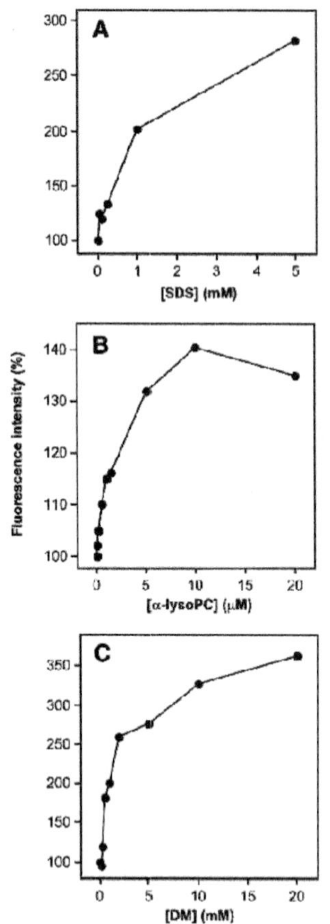

FIGURE 6: Binding of arbidol to SDS (A), α-lysoPC (B), and DM (C) at pH 5.0. Fluorescence conditions were similar to those in Figure 4. Increasing concentrations of detergent were added to a cuvette containing ARB (18.8 μM) in PBS buffer acidified at pH 5.0 and equilibrated at 37 μ C. Emission spectra for each concentration were recorded after a 5 min equilibration. The fluorescence intensities obtained after each detergent addition, corrected using blank values (detergent alone in buffer), were plotted as a percentage of the initial value, as a function of final detergent concentration.

Depending on pH, ARB may therefore exist as a deproto-nated, neutral form, or as a protonated, cationic form [see Figure 1D (22)]. ARB's position within or on detergent micelles and its intrinsic fluorescence properties may then depend on its ionization state.

Taken together, the data indicate that arbidol has tropism for membranelike environments and that this propensity to interact with hydrophobic environments is more pronounced at acidic than at neutral pH, possibly due to the ionization state of ARB.

Arbidol Has Tropism for Lipid Membranes. The interaction of ARB with liposomes was then studied at neutral and acidic pH. Results are presented in Figure 8 and Table 1. In the presence of increasing concentrations of PC/chol liposomes,

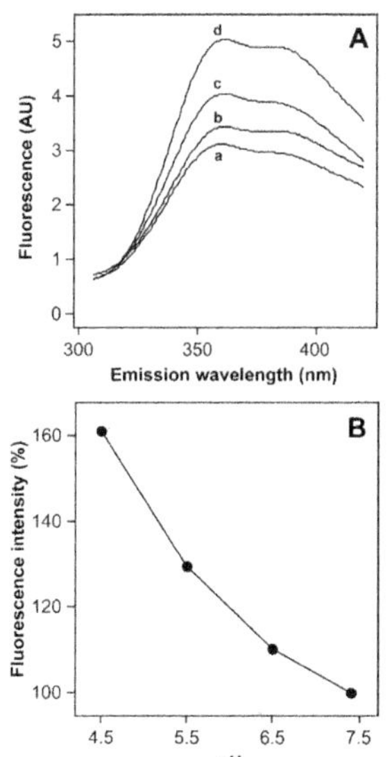

FIGURE 7: Effect of pH on binding of arbidol to DM micelles. DM (final concentration of 5 mM) was added to a 18.8 μM (10 μg/mL) ARB solution in PBS (pH 7.4). Fluorescence conditions were similar to those in Figure 4. The pH was decreased by addition of diluted HCl to the cuvette, and (A) emission spectra were recorded at pH 7.4 (a), 6.5 (b), 5.5 (c), or 4.5 (d), after a 5 min equilibration at 37 µ C. (B) Plot of the fluorescence obtained at 350 nm from panel A as a function of pH, expressed as a percentage of the initial value at pH 7.4.

λ_{max} is progressively shifted to lower wavelengths (blue shift), with a concomitant increase in quantum yield (Table 1). These changes most likely result from a significant increase in the hydrophobicity of the ARB microenvironment upon binding to liposomes. Moreover, fluorescence emission depends upon phospholipid concentration (compare curves a to c or d for each panel, Figure 8), which indicates that the ARB microenvironment becomes more hydrophobic in the presence of liposomes and therefore points toward the interaction of ARB with lipid membranes. This trend is even more pronounced at acidic pH (Figure 8B and Table 1). Indeed, larger blue shifts (up to 20 nm) were associated with greater increases in quantum yield at pH 5.0 as compared to pH 7.4, which may reflect enhanced incorporation of the ARB molecule into the hydrophobic core of lipid bilayers at low pH. This extends our previous observations that ARB inhibits fusion more prominently at acidic pH than at neutral pH in the pH-independent Ca-induced PS vesicle fusion model. In addition, for similar pH's and an ARB concentration of 10 μg/mL, much larger blue shifts are observed with liposomes than with any detergent micelles (Table 1). This indicates that the environment of ARB is significantly more hydrophobic in lipid bilayers than in micelles, i.e., that ARB reaches the hydrophobic core of the lipid bilayer whereas it is most likely associated shallowly with the surface of detergent micelles. This is consistent with the view that the fluorescent indole moiety of ARB is partially buried in the liposome membranes.

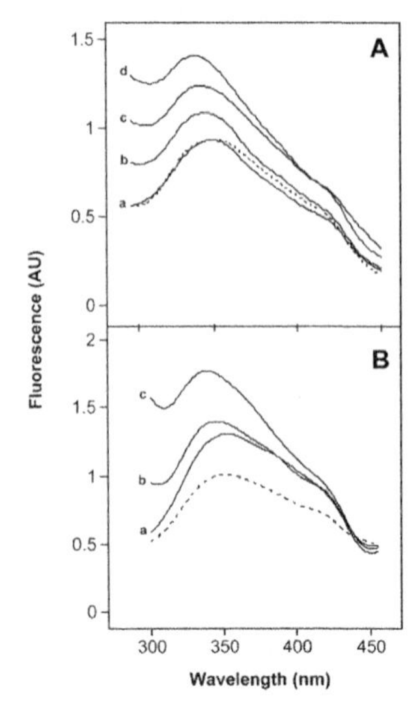

FIGURE 8: Influence of liposomes on ARB fluorescence. (A) Neutral pH. PC/chol (70:30 molar ratio) liposomes were added at 12.5 (a), 25 (b), 62.5 (c), or 100 *i*M (d) to a 18.8 μM (10 μg/mL) ARB solution in PBS pH 7.4 (dotted line). Emission spectra were recorded after incubation for 5 min and corrected for blank (buffer) and liposome scattering effects. (B) Acidic pH. An ARB solution (10 μg/mL) in PBS buffer (pH 7.4) was acidified with HCl to the pH 5.0 final reading (dotted line), and PC/chol liposomes were subsequently added [final lipid concentrations of 12.5 (a), 25 (b) or 62.5 μM (c)].

Taken together, the data provide direct evidence that ARB is incorporated into artificial lipid bilayers (liposomes), as well as biological membranes such as cellular and viral membranes, indicating that ARB inhibits entry of HCV into cells and HCV-mediated fusion by acting directly at the membrane level.

DISCUSSION

This study aimed to assess the anti-HCV properties of arbidol, a broad-spectrum Russian-made oral antiviral drug. Using HCV pseudoparticles, we analyzed the effects of ARB on HCV entry at the fusion step and demonstrated that ARB is able to inhibit this process in a dose-dependent manner.

HCV entry and membrane fusion are early steps in the life cycle of the virus (*29*, *30*). HCV first interacts through its envelope glycoproteins with a set of coreceptors at the plasma membrane level (reviewed in ref *31*) and eventually becomes endocytosed (*32*, *33*). Due to a combined action of acidification in the endosome and particular lipids like cholesterol (*16*), viral fusion occurs over a broad spectrum of pH's ranging from 6.3 to 5.0 (*16*, *24*). This suggests that fusion could occur in early as well as in late endosomes, or at least that a cascade of reorganizations could occur in the fusion protein(s) during the progression of the virus in the endocytic pathway. In this respect, the inhibitory action of ARB on HCVpp entry and fusion could be envisaged at various levels, including the viral glycoprotein, membrane, or the endosomal lumen. Viral infectivity studies with HCVpp showed that ARB exerted its inhibitory effect only when it was present throughout the course of infection and that an almost complete inhibition was achieved when the cells were preincubated with ARB (Figure 2). Similarly, ARB inhibition of primary infection of Huh7.5.1 cells with JFH-1 virus was complete only when cells were preincubated with ARB 24 or 48 h before infection (*12*). This points to an action of ARB on cell membranes and suggests that a certain level of membrane impregnation and/or saturation with ARB must be achieved to efficiently block HCV infection. HCVpp-1a-mediated in vitro fusion was completely blocked at a low ARB concentration (1 μg/mL; Figure 3). Fusion was inhibited similarly when viral envelope membranes or target (liposome) membranes were preincubated with ARB, indi-cating again an effect on membranes, although a specific effect of ARB on HCV glycoproteins themselves cannot be excluded. From a physicochemical point of view, ARB displays tropism for membranes or membranelike environments such as detergent micelles, particularly prominent at low pH (Figures 1 and 5-8 and Table 1). This may be due to ARB's indole-derived structure (Figure 1). Moreover, ARB may interact with lipids via other hydrophobic and aromatic moieties on the molecule.

With regard to detergents, ARB bound similarly at acidic pH to the micelles of all three detergents that were tested, binding being total at 10 μM α-lysoPC ($C_{16:0}$) or almost total at 1 mM SDS and at 2 mM DM. Under these conditions, most of the detergent is in a micellar form, since the cmc values for $C_{16:0}$ α-lysoPC, SDS, and DM are 6 μM (*34*), 1.2 mM, and 0.18 mM (*28*), respectively. The enhancement of ARB fluorescence is greater upon binding to DM micelles than upon binding to other detergent micelles or lipid vesicles (Table 1). The maltose headgroup of DM is rigid, giving a high level of cohesion to the headgroup region of the micelles (*35*). These maltose rings might therefore exert a stacking effect with the indole rings of ARB, leading to the observed dramatic increase in ARB fluorescence. However, we consistently observed a lack of shift toward lower wave-lengths (blue shift) in ARB fluorescence with DM micelles. At low pH, this could come from a shielding effect on the protonation of ARB, played by the numerous hydroxyl groups of DM.

With regard to lipid vesicles, ARB membrane association was accompanied by a blue shift and an increase in quantum yield of fluorescence for all ARB:lipid ratios that were tested, particularly prominent at low pH (Figure 8 and Table 1). When comparing these data to those obtained with detergent micelles, we can infer that ARB probably embeds itself more deeply into lipid bilayers than in micelles and is probably in a more hydrophobic microenvironment in bilayers than in micelles. This difference in fluorescence behavior between lipid bilayers and detergent micelles most likely comes from the very low cmc of lipids in aqueous buffers, where all lipids are in the condensed membrane phase. Compared to DM micelles more specifically, the flexible choline headgroups of PC might allow a better accessibility to the hydrophobic core of the particle (vesicle or micelle) than the rigid sugar headgroup of DM, as already described for the indole derivative tryptophan octyl ester (*36*).

Indole derivatives have been shown to exhibit a preference for membrane interfaces (*25*, *26*), due to the flat rigid structure of these molecules and to their aromaticity which allows them to establish cation-π interactions with the positively charged quaternary ammonium lipid headgroups (*25*, *27*). The *S*-phenyl groups of ARB could also interact with the hydrophobic fatty acid chains of phospholipids inside the bilayer. The amino groups could bond the phosphate moieties of phospholipids and establish a salt bridge between two adjacent phospholipid molecules as an ion pair complex. At low pH, these interactions would be favored due to the protonation of the amino groups. In particular, protonation of the 3-position could displace the ester group out of the indole plane and place it in a better position to bond with neighboring molecules (see Figure 1D). This could in turn lead to a better membrane association. Considering these chemically plausible interactions, ARB might have the propensity to intercalate into lipids in the membrane while adopting a consistent orientation by filling the gaps between lipid molecules. The molar ratio between ARB and lipids in our in vitro fusion assays is ca. 1:10, so a plausible mode of action could be the formation of a stable and dose-dependent "ARB cage" at the surface of mem-branes, and therefore to excessive stabilization of these membranes, which become resistant to fusion. This mode of action would be quite reminiscent to that observed for the tripeptide inhibiting fusion, carbobenzoxy-D-phenylalanyl-L-phenylalanylglycine Z-fFG. Z-fFG was shown to inhibit viral fusion by stabilizing bilayers in their lamellar phase, thereby inhibiting nonbilayer phase formation most likely from the surface of the bilayer, i.e., not by forming a tight complex with phospholipids (*37-39*). The carbobenzoxy group is important for the effectiveness of fusion inhibition (*38*); it is interesting to note that ARB contains a phenyl-thio-methyl group in position 2 of the indole ring, which could play a role comparable to that of the carboben-zoxy of Z-fFG in the fusion inhibition. Z-fFG inhibition of the formation of highly curved surfaces, occurring during membrane fusion, was found to be more effective at low pH where the protonated form of the tripeptide is predominant (*39*). This correlates well with ARB behavior as observed in our study, where the protonated form might as well penetrate deeper into the membrane than the charged form.

This hypothesis of membrane stabilization as a mode of action of ARB in the viral fusion system finds support from the PS/Ca model system, since ARB also blocks fusion in this membrane system, and again more efficiently at low than at neutral pH (Figure 3). The PS/Ca model also provides the information that ARB can inhibit fusion at neutral pH, which could be an explanation for the ARB inhibition of fusion of pH-independent viruses such as some paramyx-oviruses and coronaviruses (*8*).

At the virus level, ARB might block the uncoating of the membrane during the fusion process. From our infection and fusion data, we cannot exclude a direct action of ARB on endosomal pH and/or on HCV glycoproteins. On the basis of its chemical structure, ARB is a weak base that could undergo hydrolysis of its ester function in vivo. For these reasons, ARB could exert its effect on HCVpp infection and fusion through inhibition of the acidification in the endo-somes, and/or through accumulation of hydrolyzed ARB molecules. The first hypothesis was tested directly by measuring the pH of a liposome/HCVpp suspension under the conditions of our fusion assay. Even at very high ARB concentrations, we could not detect any significant variation in pH. A behavior of ARB as an ionophore or as a blocker of proton pumps inside the endosome cannot be excluded in vivo. However, if this effect were operative, it would unlikely be the predominant mechanism of action of the molecule, since ARB inhibits pH-dependent and pH-independent viruses with a similar efficacy (*8*), and we showed in this study that ARB could block fusion in the pH-independent Ca-induced PS vesicle fusion system. The second hypothesis of ARB hydrolysis in vivo followed by intracellular accumulation of the cleaved compound finds support from our results that ARB displayed optimal activity when administered 24-48 h before primary HCV infection (*12*), or preincubated 3 h with cells before HCVpp infection (this study).

We also reproducibly noticed that ARB inhibition of cell entry and/or fusion concerned HCVpp and HApp, but not RD114pp (Figures 2 and 3). This suggests that ARB might display specificity for the recognition of key motifs inside the fusion protein, leading to inhibition of the properties of this protein. Furthermore, HCVpp fusion was more pro-nounced on genotype 1a-derived than on genotype 1b and 2a-derived pseudoparticles (Figure 3). Since different HCV genotypes possess sequence variability, it is conceivable that ARB might differently affect fusion induced by genetically different glycoproteins. In our fusion assay, liposomes are devoid of HCV receptors; therefore, subtle changes in envelope protein conformation between genotypes might affect fusion more than infectivity, since receptors could help in conformational rearrangements at the plasma membrane of cells. Since ARB is most likely able to enter into a number of chemical interactions with lipid molecules, these interac-tions might exist for ARB/HCV glycoprotein(s) as well. Hydrophobic interactions, formation of salt bridges, and cation-π interactions govern the binding of several ligands to proteins (e.g., ref *27*). This hypothesis cannot be tested experimentally at present in the absence of any three-dimensional structure of HCV E1 and E2. However, further studies using the recently described genotype 1a (*40*) and chimeric (*41*) infectious culture systems may provide further insight into the mechanisms accounting for the possible genotype-specific effects of ARB.

Arbidol also exerted a clear inhibitory effect on HCV replication, with loss of protein expression and a decline in the RNA level (*12*). This effect was visible after cells containing an HCV-1b replicon had been treated for 2 weeks, and no rebound effect was observed after removal of the drug (*12*). Since this replicon did not produce infectious particles, the antiviral effects of ARB in this system cannot involve inhibition of virus fusion and infectivity. The HCV replication complex associates with endoplasmic reticulum (ER) membranes to form membranous webs (*42*). The web is formed via the association of HCV nonstructural proteins with ER membranes (*43, 44*). One can therefore speculate that ARB-induced inhibition of interactions of HCV non-structural protein with organelle membranes that are required for HCV replication might also contribute to ARB's anti-HCV actions.

Current interferon-based anti-HCV therapies have shown their limits, since 40-50% of patients do not achieve sustained viral eradication with IFN treatment (*45*). A number of antiviral strategies against HCV are presently being developed, some of which are directed against viral enzymes or viral genome or aimed at modulating the host immune response (*46*). Recently, two groups described the anti-HCV replication activity of small molecules that perturb the intracellular lipid metabolism. Sakamoto and co-workers (*47*) described the activity of NA255, which prevents the de novo synthesis of sphingolipids and thus disrupts the association of HCV nonstructural proteins on the lipid rafts. Pezacki's group studied the anti-HCV effect of an antagonist of the peroxisome proliferator-activated receptor (PPAR) (*48*). Inhibition of PPAR led to HCV inhibition of replication through dysregulation of lipid metabolism, phospholipid secretion, cholesterol catabolism, and triglyceride clearance.

Thus, lipids and membranes are clearly central to the HCV life cycle, where each step is directly related to membrane activity. Arbidol, by its tropism for membranes and its inhibitory effect on HCV entry, fusion, and replication, opens promising perspectives in the search for new and efficient anti-HCV therapies.

ACKNOWLEDGMENT

We gratefully acknowledge Dr. François Penin (IBCP, Lyon, France) for continuous support, critical reading, and helpful discussions at several stages of the manuscript. E.-I.P. thanks Elodie Teissier for technical assistance. Fluores-cence measurements were performed at ªProduction et Analyse physico-chimique des Protéines° (PAP) of the IFR128 BioSciences Lyon Gerland.

REFERENCES

1. Di Bisceglie, A. M., Fan, X., Chambers, T., and Strinko, J. (2006) Pharmacokinetics, pharmacodynamics, and hepatitis C viral kinet-ics during antiviral therapy: The null responder, *J. Med. Virol. 78*, 446-451.
2. Lohmann, V., Korner, F., Koch, J., Herian, U., Theilmann, L., and Bartenschlager, R. (1999) Replication of subgenomic hepatitis
   Cvirus RNAs in a hepatoma cell line, *Science 285*, 110-113.
3. Horscroft, N., Lai, V. C., Cheney, W., Yao, N., Wu, J. Z., Hong, Z., and Zhong, W. (2005) Replicon cell culture system as a valuable tool in antiviral drug discovery against hepatitis C virus,
   AntiViral Chem. Chemother. 16, 1-12.
4. Paeshuyse, J., Kaul, A., De Clercq, E., Rosenwirth, B., Dumont,
   J.M., Scalfaro, P., Bartenschlager, R., and Neyts, J. (2006) The non-immunosuppressive cyclosporin DEBIO-025 is a potent inhibitor of hepatitis C virus replication in vitro, *Hepatology 43*, 761-770.
5. Duong, F. H., Christen, V., Filipowicz, M., and Heim, M. H. (2006) S-Adenosylmethionine and betaine correct hepatitis C virus induced inhibition of interferon signaling in vitro, *Hepatology 43*, 796-806.
6. Anonymous (1999) Arbidol, *Drugs R&D 2*, 171-172.
7. Gagarinova, V. M., Ignat'eva, G. S., Sinitskaia, L. V., Ivanova,
   A.M., Rodina, M. A., and Tur'eva, A. V. (1993) (The new chemical preparation arbidol: Its prophylactic efficacy during influenza epidemics), *Zh. Mikrobiol., Epidemiol. Immunobiol.*, 40-43.
8. Brooks, M. J., Sasadeusz, J. J., and Tannock, G. A. (2004) Antiviral chemotherapeutic agents against respiratory viruses: Where are we now and what's in the pipeline? *Curr. Opin. Pulm. Med. 10*, 197-203.
9. Chai, H., Zhao, Y., Zhao, C., and Gong, P. (2006) Synthesis and in vitro anti-hepatitis B virus activities of some ethyl 6-bromo-5-hydroxy-1H-indole-3-carboxylates, *Bioorg. Med. Chem. 14*, 911-917.
10. Fediakina, I. T., Leneva, I. A., Iamnikova, S. S., Livov, D. K., Glushkov, R. G., and Shuster, A. M. (2005) (Sensitivity of influenza A/H5 viruses isolated from wild birds on the territory of Russia to arbidol in the cultured MDCK cells), *Vopr. Virusol. 50*, 32-35.
11. Leneva, I. A., Fediakina, I. T., Gus'kova, T. A., and Glushkov,
    R.G. (2005) (Sensitivity of various influenza virus strains to arbidol. Influence of arbidol combination with different antiviral drugs on reproduction of influenza virus A), *Ter. Arkh. 77*, 84-88.
12. Boriskin, Y. S., Pécheur, E. I., and Polyak, S. J. (2006) Arbidol: a broad-spectrum antiviral that inhibits acute and chronic HCV infection, *Virol. J. 3*, 56.

13. Bartosch, B., Dubuisson, J., and Cosset, F. L. (2003) Infectious hepatitis C virus pseudo-particles containing functional E1-E2 envelope protein complexes, *J. Exp. Med. 197*, 633-642.
14. Hatziioannou, T., Valsesia-Wittmann, S., Russell, S. J., and Cosset, F.L. (1998) Incorporation of fowl plague virus hemagglutinin into murine leukemia virus particles and analysis of the infectivity of the pseudotyped retroviruses, *J. Virol. 72*, 5313-5317.
15. Sandrin, V., Boson, B., Salmon, P., Gay, W., Negre, D., Le Grand, R., Trono, D., and Cosset, F. L. (2002) Lentiviral vectors pseudotyped with a modified RD114 envelope glycoprotein show increased stability in sera and augmented transduction of primary lymphocytes and CD34+ cells derived from human and nonhuman primates, *Blood 100*, 823-832.
16. Lavillette, D., Bartosch, B., Nourrisson, D., Verney, G., Cosset, F.L., Penin, F., and Pécheur, E. I. (2006) Hepatitis C Virus Glycoproteins Mediate Low pH-dependent Membrane Fusion with Liposomes, *J. Biol. Chem. 281*, 3909-3917.
17. Ladokhin, A. S., Jayasinghe, S., and White, S. H. (2000) How to measure and analyze tryptophan fluorescence in membranes properly, and why bother? *Anal. Biochem. 285*, 235-245.
18. Pécheur, E. I., Martin, I., Ruysschaert, J. M., Bienvenue, A., and Hoekstra, D. (1998) Membrane fusion induced by 11-mer anionic and cationic peptides: A structure-function study, *Biochemistry 37*, 2361-2371.
19. Wilschut, J., and Papahadjopoulos, D. (1979) Ca^{2+}-induced fusion of phospholipid vesicles monitored by mixing of aqueous contents. *Nature 281*, 690-692.
20. Breisblatt, W., and Ohki, S. (1976) Fusion in phospholipid spherical membranes. II. Effect of cholesterol, divalent ions and pH, *J. Membr. Biol. 29*, 127-146.
21. Savarino, A., Boelaert, J. R., Cassone, A., Majori, G., and Cauda, R. (2003) Effects of chloroquine on viral infections: An old drug against today's diseases? *Lancet Infect. Dis. 3*, 722-727.
22. Hinman, R. L., and Lang, J. (1964) The Protonation of Indoles. Basicity Studies. The Dependence of Acidity Functions on Indicator Structure, *J. Am. Chem. Soc. 86*, 3796-3806.
23. Stegmann, T., Hoekstra, D., Scherphof, G., and Wilschut, J. (1985) Kinetics of pH-dependent fusion between influenza virus and liposomes, *Biochemistry 24*, 3107-3113.
24. Kobayashi, M., Bennett, M. C., Bercot, T., and Singh, I. R. (2006) Functional analysis of hepatitis C virus envelope proteins, using a cell-cell fusion assay, *J. Virol. 80*, 1817-1825.
25. Petersen, F. N., Jensen, M. O., and Nielsen, C. H. (2005) Interfacial tryptophan residues: A role for the cation-$\eth$ effect? *Biophys. J. 89*, 3985-3996.
26. Yau, W. M., Wimley, W. C., Gawrisch, K., and White, S. H. (1998) The preference of tryptophan for membrane interfaces, *Biochemistry 37*, 14713-14718.
27. Zacharias, N., and Dougherty, D. A. (2002) Cation-$\eth$ interactions in ligand recognition and catalysis, *Trends Pharmacol. Sci. 23*, 281-287.
28. le Maire, M., Champeil, P., and Moller, J. V. (2000) Interaction of membrane proteins and lipids with solubilizing detergents, *Biochim. Biophys. Acta 1508*, 86-111.
29. Bartenschlager, R., and Lohmann, V. (2000) Replication of hepatitis C virus, *J. Gen. Virol. 81*, 1631-1648.
30. Lindenbach, B. D., and Rice, C. M. (2005) Unravelling hepatitis virus replication from genome to function, *Nature 436*, 933-938.
31. Bartosch, B., and Cosset, F. L. (2006) Cell entry of hepatitis C virus, *Virology 348*, 1-12.

32. Bartosch, B., Vitelli, A., Granier, C., Goujon, C., Dubuisson, J., Pascale, S., Scarselli, E., Cortese, R., Nicosia, A., and Cosset, F.L. (2003) Cell Entry of Hepatitis C Virus Requires a Set of Co-receptors That Include the CD81 Tetraspanin and the SR-B1 Scavenger Receptor, *J. Biol. Chem. 278*, 41624-41630.
33. Tscherne, D. M., Jones, C. T., Evans, M. J., Lindenbach, B. D., McKeating, J. A., and Rice, C. M. (2006) Time- and temperature-dependent activation of hepatitis C virus for low-pH-triggered entry, *J. Virol. 80*, 1734-1741.
34. Kumar, V. V., and Baumann, W. J. (1991) Lanthanide-induced phosphorus-31 NMR downfield chemical shifts of lysophosphati-dylcholines are sensitive to lysophospholipid critical micelle concentration, *Biophys. J. 59*, 103-107.
35. Tortech, L., Jaxel, C., Vincent, M., Gallay, J., and de Foresta, B. (2001) The polar headgroup of the detergent governs the acces-sibility to water of tryptophan octyl ester in host micelles, *Biochim. Biophys. Acta 1514*, 76-86.
36. de Foresta, B., Gallay, J., Sopkova, J., Champeil, P., and Vincent, M. (1999) Tryptophan octyl ester in detergent micelles of dodecylmaltoside: Fluorescence properties and quenching by brominated detergent analogs, *Biophys. J. 77*, 3071-3084.
37. Yeagle, P. L., Dentino, A. R., Smith, F. T., Spooner, P., and Watts, A. (1993) The antiviral peptide carbobenzoxy-D-phenylalanyl-L-phenylalanylglycine changes the average conformation of phos-pholipids in membranes, *Biochemistry 32*, 12197-12202.
38. Epand, R. M., Epand, R. F., Richardson, C. D., and Yeagle, P. L. (1993) Structural requirements for the inhibition of membrane fusion by carbobenzoxy-D-Phe-Phe-Gly, *Biochim. Biophys. Acta 1152*, 128-134.
39. Dentino, A. R., Westerman, P. W., and Yeagle, P. L. (1995) A study of carbobenzoxy-D-phenylalanine-L-phenylalanine-glycine, an inhibitor of membrane fusion, in phospholipid bilayers with multinuclear magnetic resonance, *Biochim. Biophys. Acta 1235*, 213-220.
40. Yi, M., Villanueva, R. A., Thomas, D. L., Wakita, T., and Lemon, S.M. (2006) Production of infectious genotype 1a hepatitis C virus (Hutchinson strain) in cultured human hepatoma cells, *Proc. Natl. Acad. Sci. U.S.A. 103*, 2310-2315.
41. Pietschmann, T., Kaul, A., Koutsoudakis, G., Shavinskaya, A., Kallis, S., Steinmann, E., Abid, K., Negro, F., Dreux, M., Cosset, F.L., and Bartenschlager, R. (2006) Construction and characterization of infectious intragenotypic and intergenotypic hepatitis C virus chimeras, *Proc. Natl. Acad. Sci. U.S.A. 103*, 7408-7413.
42. Moradpour, D., Gosert, R., Egger, D., Penin, F., Blum, H. E., and Bienz, K. (2003) Membrane association of hepatitis C virus nonstructural proteins and identification of the membrane alteration that harbors the viral replication complex, *AntiViral Res. 60*, 103-109.
43. Appel, N., Schaller, T., Penin, F., and Bartenschlager, R. (2006) From structure to function: New insights into hepatitis C virus RNA replication, *J. Biol. Chem. 281*, 9833-9836.
44. Gretton, S. N., Taylor, A. I., and McLauchlan, J. (2005) Mobility of the hepatitis C virus NS4B protein on the endoplasmic reticulum membrane and membrane-associated foci, *J. Gen. Virol. 86*, 1415-1421.
45. Feld, J. J., and Hoofnagle, J. H. (2005) Mechanism of action of interferon and ribavirin in treatment of hepatitis C, *Nature 436*, 967-972.
46. De Francesco, R., and Migliaccio, G. (2005) Challenges and successes in developing new therapies for hepatitis C, *Nature 436*, 953-960.

47. Sakamoto, H., Okamoto, K., Aoki, M., Kato, H., Katsume, A., Ohta, A., Tsukuda, T., Shimma, N., Aoki, Y., Arisawa, M., Kohara, M., and Sudoh, M. (2005) Host sphingolipid biosynthesis as a target for hepatitis C virus therapy, *Nat. Chem. Biol. 1*, 333-337.
48. Rakic, B., Sagan, S. M., Noestheden, M., Belanger, S., Nan, X., Evans, C. L., Xie, X. S., and Pezacki, J. P. (2006) Peroxisome proliferator-activated receptor R antagonism inhibits hepatitis C virus replication, *Chem. Biol. 13*, 23-30.

REFERENCES

Mechanism of inhibition of Enveloped Virus Membrane Fusion by the Antiviral Drug Arbidol.
Teissier E, Zandomeneghi G, Loquet A, Lavillette D, Lavergne JP, Montserret R, Cosset FL, Böckmann A, Meier BH, Penin F, Pécheur EI.
PLoS One.
2011 Jan 25;6(1):e15874.

La molécule antivirale arbidol inhibe des virus pathogènes de prévalence mondiale
Eve-Isabelle Pécheur & Stephen J. Polyak
Médecine Sciences (Paris).
2016 Dec;32(12):1056-1059.

The Synthetic Antiviral Drug Arbidol Inhibits Globally Prevalent Pathogenic Viruses
Pécheur EI, Borisevich V, Halfmann P, Morrey JD, Smee DF, Prichard M, Mire CE, Kawaoka Y, Geisbert TW, Polyak SJ.
Journal of Virology.
2016 Jan 6;90(6):3086-92.

Arbidol inhibits viral entry by interfering with clathrin-dependent trafficking
Blaising J, Lévy PL, Polyak SJ, Stanifer M, Boulant S, Pécheur EI.
Antiviral Research.
2013 Oct;100(1):215-9.

Arbidol as a broad-spectrum antiviral: An update
Blaising J, Polyak SJ, Pécheur EI.
Antiviral Research.
2014 Jul;107:84-94.

Biochemical Mechanism of Hepatitis C Virus Inhibition by the Broad-Spectrum Antiviral Arbidol
Pécheur EI, Lavillette D, Alcaras F, Molle J, Boriskin YS, Roberts M, Cosset FL, Polyak SJ.
Biochemistry.
2007 May 22;46(20):6050-9.

Printed in Great Britain
by Amazon